# OUTSOURCING

# MRO

## FINDING A BETTER WAY

—— BY GEORGE KRAUTER ——

*To CARLOS*
*THANKS FOR THE OPPORTUNITY*
*George (TWO WEEKS EARLY)*
*Krauter*

**RELIA BILITY®**
**WEB.COM**

# OUTSOURCING MRO
# FINDING A BETTER WAY

by George Krauter

ISBN 978-1-941872-40-6
HF032016

Publisher: Terrence O'Hanlon
Design and Layout: Jocelyn Brown

For information: Reliabilityweb.com
www.reliabilityweb.com
8991 Daniels Center Drive, Suite 105, Ft. Myers, FL 33912
Toll Free: 888-575-1245 | Phone: 239-333-2500
E-mail: customerservice@reliabilityweb.com

10   9   8   7   6   5   4   3   2   1

*I have never met any person more knowledgeable or passionate about MRO as George Krauter. Forever the storyteller, he weaves humorous, yet relevant, tales to teach the world about the value and importance of the materials maintaining and repairing a facility. His breadth of knowledge and ability to connect importance to the larger picture is one he is eager to share in hopes of sparking MRO passion in others.*

Diane Caldwell, Sr. Director, Project Management Office
Storeroom Solutions, Inc.

*What a read!! Having been in the MRO business for 36 years, I found that this book has captured the many factors that have impacted our industry and brought it to where it is today. This is a "must" read for those who don't really understand the importance of a solid MRO supply base and the effect it has on a company's overall performance.*

Tom Melina, Vice President
MRO Logistix

*After 17 years in the MRO procurement business, it is clear to me that very few understand the complexity of the highly fragmented world of MRO. Typical behaviors and direct procurement methods have failed to consistently deliver material value to customers. I wondered how to approach MRO from a strategic perspective without disrupting critical supply to operations... until I met George Krauter; he saw the corporate MRO struggle long before it was identified by those suffering from it. Seizing the opportunity, George forged a new industry out of his vision for a strategic solution that, today, is known as Third Party Integrated Supply. I can't thank George enough for what he has done for me personally as a mentor and advocate, and what he has done for the advancement of American industry.*

Alisha M. Moss, CEO
VM3 Consulting Corporation

*George has seen the good, the bad and the downright ugly in MRO throughout his career. His insight, perspective and solutions are spot on. I always appreciate the opportunity to talk shop and hear the lessons he has learned along the way.*

Scott West, Vice President, Supply Chain
Storeroom Solutions, Inc.

*George's business expertise and depth of experience provide an excellent foundation for the "Outsourcing MRO Finding A Better Way." Real world insights and guidance are very important to practitioners, supply chain students and C-Suite leaders; this book can be a valuable guide to..."Finding a Better Way".*

Jim Haddow, Director,
Center for Excellence in Supply Chain Management
Howard University School of Business
Washington DC 20059

# TABLE OF CONTENTS

# ACKNOWLEDGMENTS

T his book contains very few references to sources of information because the data contained represent over fifty years of MRO experiences, knowledge and contributions afforded me from individuals to whom I owe the success and well-being of my life in the turbulent world of MRO. This real-world intelligence has been gained from being there with very talented people; it is how MRO really is.

The following people have made this book possible:

- ➢ Joyce Krauter, Industrial Systems Associates, Inc.
- ➢ Andrea Krauter Hogan, Industrial Systems Associates, Inc.
- ➢ Kenneth Krauter, Industrial Systems Associates, Inc.
- ➢ Kim Brown Krauter, Consultant
- ➢ Joe Hogan, Finance
- ➢ Bruce Leonard, Industrial Systems Associates, Inc.
- ➢ Jackie Fox (Dec.), Industrial Systems Associates, Inc.
- ➢ Linda Brunner, Industrial Systems Associates, Inc.
- ➢ Terry Doyle (Dec.), Risk Taker
- ➢ Ralph Bolton, Author, "Systems Contracting"
- ➢ David Smith, Siemens AG
- ➢ Alisha Moss, VM3 Consulting
- ➢ Carlos Tellez, Storeroom Solutions
- ➢ Dan Brennan, Storeroom Solutions
- ➢ Diane Caldwell, Storeroom Solutions

- Ed McFadden (Ret.), Storeroom Solutions

- Hector Caballero (Dec.), Storeroom Solutions

- Larry Newhart, Storeroom Solutions

- Mike Dyson, Storeroom Solutions

- Mike Weinberg, Storeroom Solutions

- James Haddow, Howard University

- Andrew Bursky, Atlas Holdings

- Cathy James, Investor

- Temple University and the GI Bill

- Krauter Hardware

- Rachel Janssen, for without her, this book would be handwritten

**NOTE:** For examples of MRO scenarios, references are made to "U.S. Flan, the Best Dang Flan in the World" and T.M. Doyle, CFO of U.S. Flan. While this company is fictitious, the situations described are real, and so was Terrance Michael (T.M.) Patrick Doyle.

# INTRODUCTION

*Dilettante – a person who will cultivate areas of interest without commitment or knowledge. There are dilettantes in the world of MRO operations.*

Once upon a time, someone coined the acronym MRO for maintenance, repair and operations supplies. MRO can be described as one of the most misunderstood, most maligned and most ignored functions that exists in the manufacturing and process industries.

Your company has established a substantial investment in a plan designed to provide reliable and sustainable equipment (assets) to enable its operations to optimize production and reach corporate goals. To do so requires world-class maintenance proficiency that will provide a reliable plant operation. In turn, a reliable, world-class maintenance program requires a world-class MRO storeroom operation, otherwise the investment will not be successful. A fat, inefficient, unresponsive and unconnected storeroom will substantially detract from the investment your company has made in lean maintenance activities.

The major goal of this book is to increase your knowledge regarding the real world of MRO that exists, while establishing a higher level of awareness of the values that can be released through a change to optimum in your MRO mode of operations.

Many veterans in various phases of industry will point to their years of service and experience as proof that they are experts; they consider anyone with fewer years of experience to be lacking. They state: "I've been in this business for forty years and I know how it should be done."

I have been in all stations of the MRO supply chain for fifty years; the only thing I'm sure of is that I have not seen the last of change, nor have I seen the last opportunity to improve.

# THE MRO WORLD

## THE HISTORY

The history of the MRO supply chain can be traced back to the supply of materials from the manufacturers who sold directly to the users, such as farmers and ship chandlers. With the Industrial Revolution, there were too many consumers for the manufacturers to supply economically on a direct basis, therefore, they sold to local "general" stores which, in turn, became retail hardware stores. These hardware stores purchased their wares from manufacturers at a discount and sold them as retailers to consumers with a markup for profit. This economic growth caused the larger hardware stores to shut down their retail markets and sell to industry only, thus the creation of the industrial distribution industry.

Today, the industrial distribution industry supplies maintenance, repair and operations materials to industry, institutions and miscellaneous commercial end users. This industry is typified by many small companies or providers with relatively few large players. In the next chapter, MRO is separated into twenty categories, which are represented by non-competing distributors who specialize in their particular area of expertise. Exceptions are those distributors/companies that combine category offerings in an attempt to be a single source supplier/ provider.

Manufacturers that sell via distributors do so because of the economics necessary to reach the large number of commercial clients (MRO consumers). They do so by extending a functional discount to their authorized distributors; this functional discount is not available to the end user.

Large MRO consumers create and manage their storerooms in an effort to have parts on hand when needed to support their operations. These operations constitute duplications in the supply chain which, in turn, cause additional costs when the products are consumed by the end users within those companies.

The industrial distribution industry is structured with duplicated functions, conflicting goals and personal differences among company disciplines. Manufacturers selling via distributors espouse policies that are continually adjusted based upon subjective considerations from particular markets. Relationships with clients/customers are based upon the profit motive (e.g., whoever can get the most from whom and still retain continuing revenue).

Here are the conditions that exist in this market:

- $500 billion annual consumption;
- Average distributor yearly sales: $20 million;
- Few large, dominant distributors;
- Populated with full line distributors offering all MRO categories and specialty distributors who concentrate on specific MRO categories;
- Competing distributors with essentially the same sales and marketing offerings: "We have good prices, large inventories and great service, so give us the order;"
- Sales and marketing efforts affected by personal relationships among buyers, engineers and distributor salespeople;
- Large MRO consumers with multiple facilities who have a corporate purchasing function to get quotes from competing distributors to obtain the best cost and service provider; generally the low price bidder is chosen because purchasing assumes that services offered by the competitors are equal;
- Expansion of the concept of integrated supply with varying degrees of success and a myriad of definitions as to what constitutes an integrated supply program.

- Expansion of e-procurement in the MRO arena as a method of placing orders with suppliers.

There are just two MRO providers that are "pure" integrators, in that all revenue comes from on site programs and related services. These companies do not participate in the traditional industrial distribution revenue stream.

## TO SUMMARIZE

As industrial manufacturing plants grew, the creation of MRO storerooms became recognized as a necessity to support a reliable plant process. Storerooms were established in order to have parts on hand when needed. Manufacturers of MRO parts established local distributors to supply the local factory storerooms. The established storeroom constitutes duplication in the MRO chain of distribution since the company's MRO store itself is a cost factor in the supply chain.

Management considers MRO as a necessary evil and pays little attention to the costs of internal distribution. The dedication of company assets to MRO distribution is a detriment to the company's core business; restocking and stores' operational costs are substantial relative to the value of the material consumed. The duplication of distributor functions in the MRO chain represents opportunity for dramatic cost reductions for the using company.

# MRO: WHAT IS IT? WHERE IS IT?

## MRO DEFINED

MRO can be described as any material the company purchases that DOES NOT go into the product produced and is not capitalized by that using company. For example, if you manufacture forklift trucks, you purchase these categories of material: tires, steering wheels, metals, wires, fasteners, paints, etc., to assemble the truck. These products are production items and are not MRO. If the paint is used to paint the truck for sale, it is classified as production; if it is used to paint a wall, it is MRO. If the company purchases a piece of machinery (i.e., an asset that is amortized), it is not MRO, however, replacement/repair parts for that asset, commonly called critical spares, are MRO.

## MRO – WHAT IS IT?

Companies, as well as individuals, will place MRO into varying classifications. These are the MRO categories that will be referenced in this book.

- ➤ Abrasives
- ➤ Adhesives
- ➤ Bearings
- ➤ Cutting Tools
- ➤ Electrical
- ➤ Fasteners
- ➤ Hand & Power Tools
- ➤ Hydraulics
- ➤ HVAC
- ➤ Gases

- ➤ Janitorial Supplies
- ➤ Lubricants
- ➤ Office Supplies
- ➤ Paint & Accessories
- ➤ Pipes-Valves-Fittings
- ➤ Pneumatics
- ➤ Power Transmission
- ➤ Safety Supplies
- ➤ Spare Parts for Assets (OEM)
- ➤ Welding Supplies

Definitions of what MRO is will differ among companies. This is a major reason why companies do not have an accurate dollar figure on what they spend on MRO. For example, a water company did not classify electrical as MRO, which altered its MRO spend figure substantially.

## MRO – WHERE IS IT?

MRO inventory is generally considered to be the dollar value of parts in the MRO storeroom. The cost of inventory is calculated based on these values. However, if inventory costs are tracked throughout the MRO supply chain, they must include the multiple duplications that exist.

The MRO manufacturer has finished goods inventory. The MRO distributor has a master distributor function with inventory and redistributes inventory to its local distribution points, who also have inventory. The distributor's clients order materials needed to operate their businesses, which goes into their MRO storerooms (more inventory). Since MRO storerooms are considered unreliable, maintenance managers will create substocks of parts they consider to be critical to do their jobs. Companies do not consider these substocks as inventory, but just ask a manager if you can take these parts home and the answer will be "No," so they do have value, therefore,parts existing in substocks should be considered as inventory.

A truck manufacturer moved its operation South including all plant assets [yes, MRO inventory also]. When the plant was vacated, $980,000 in uncontrolled MRO materials was found in desks, cabinets, and in various sub storage spots throughout the facility. Although expensed, it was still valuable "inventory" that was out of control and duplicated in the MRO storeroom.

*The point?* Inventory duplications abound in the MRO supply chain. If duplications can be reduced, the total cost of ownership (TCO) for the MRO consumer can be reduced.

# THE SITUATION

*"Investments in MRO stores' operations are investments in failure"*
– T.M. Doyle

*"Success is being able to go from failure to failure without loss of enthusiasm"*
– Winston Churchill

**Here is the situation in the typical MRO storeroom.**

➢ MRO expenditures represent six to ten percent of total purchasing dollars

➢ MRO creates eighty percent of total transactions generated

➢ MRO inventory turns less than once per year

➢ Restocking and store operations costs are substantial relative to the value of the material

➢ MRO consumers are forced to distribute MRO parts internally to the detriment of their core business

➢ Management will not allocate dollars to improve MRO service

➢ Frequent stock outs occur, resulting in downtime that causes emergencies

➢ No markups applied to issued parts

➢ The unreliable MRO operation is a drag on lean/reliability efforts

➢ Maintenance and store operations remain uncoordinated

**MRO buy is generally unstructured because of:**

➢ Considerable paperwork for little value;

➢ Inadequate record keeping;

➢ Many unrelated commodities;

➢ Numerous suppliers;

➢ Unpredictable demand;

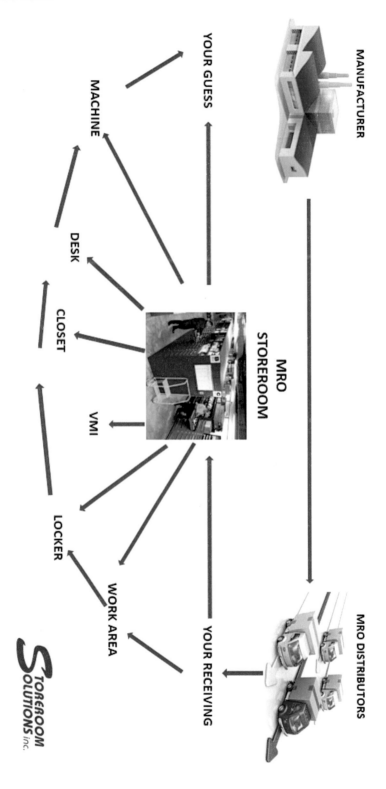

Figure 1.1: MRO: Where Is It?

➤ Storeroom inventory only supplies fifty percent of requests;

➤ Fifty percent of parts used are onetime spot buys;

➤ Spot buy prices are generally controlled by suppliers and are not measured;

➤ When MRO categories are quoted via market baskets, suppliers' margins expand on unquoted parts.

**Why does this condition continue to exist?**

➤ Adversarial relationships among departments and with suppliers

➤ Antiquated pricing and quoting policies

➤ Committee longevity

➤ Concentration on high dollar activities

➤ Entrenched suppliers

➤ Exclusive brand names

➤ Failure of distributors to provide measurable solutions

➤ Inadequate request for quotations (RFQs) that produce little improvement

➤ Job protection

➤ Lack of confidence in new distributor/supplier relationships

➤ Lack of distributor recognition of the real cost of MRO to user

➤ Lack of knowledge on how to implement change

➤ Lack of recognition that MRO represents a major cost reduction opportunity

➤ No allocation of dollars to expand stores' activities

➤ Personnel subjectivity

➤ Present business mechanics

➤ Total concentration on price as a measurement of supplier's performance

**Duplicated supply chain functions**

MRO materials are duplicated in various locations throughout the supply chain. These locations include the manufacturer's finished goods stock, stocks maintained by the authorized master distributor of the manufacturer's products, and the local distributor's inventory purchased from the master distributor. There are five other locations where MRO exists, but aren't recognized as functions of the MRO supply chain. These locations include:

1. In transit to the client, such as with a local delivery service;
2. In receiving;
3. In a staging area;
4. In stock locations in the MRO store;
5. In uncontrolled substocks throughout the facility (i.e., backup because of an unreliable MRO storeroom operation).

These supply chain duplications constitute a major increase in cost when the products finally reach their point of consumption.

# THE MRO SURVEY RESULTS

A study of MRO operations by Pennsylvania-based Storeroom Solutions, Inc., finds a lack of planning and tracking of inventory, a general lack of communication among company divisions and a lack of technology utilization. The conclusion derived from this study data indicates a change in current MRO operational management is essential for stopping the MRO drag on profitability. Survey highlights include:

- Lack of inventory tracking/security;
- Lack of maintenance planning resulting in downtime/reliability issues for more than twenty percent of those surveyed;
- Major disconnect between the storeroom, purchasing and the rest of the company;
- Technology underutilized or nonexistent;
- Major challenges that include:
  - Lack of training – personnel optimization
  - Lack of standardization or unified purchasing system
  - Lack of MRO operations knowledge
  - Lack of adequate parts descriptions – standardization.

## NOTABLE SUPPLY CHAIN DATA FROM THE STORE-ROOM SOLUTIONS, INC. STUDY:

- 55.10% are doing business with more than 50 MRO/indirect suppliers; 31.63% are doing business with more than 100

**Figure 1.2:** Traditional MRO Supply Chain... Six Areas of Inventory Duplication

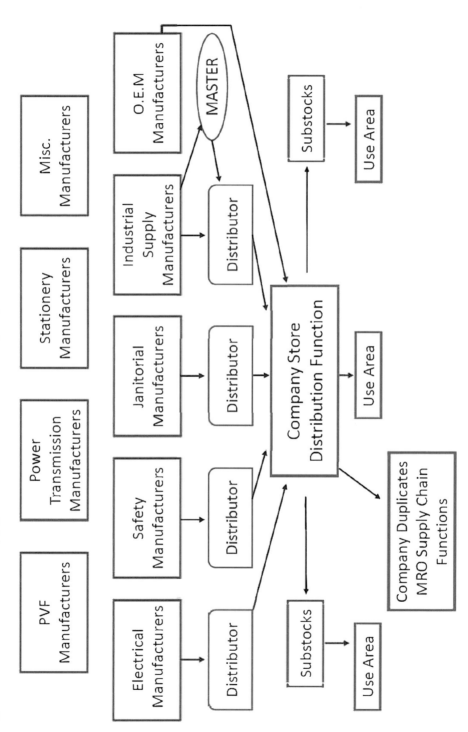

- 31.63% indicated the number of supplies are going from increasing to rapidly increasing
- 64.29% manage their supply chain using long-term agreements with important MRO suppliers
  - Note: These are price only agreements that do not recognize total cost of ownership (TCO) reduction opportunities.
- 60.20% indicated their MRO/indirect materials storeroom rarely or never causes reliability issues or downtime, therefore, 40% of downtime is caused by an unreliable MRO storeroom
- 22.11% of companies surveyed want to reduce their total MRO/indirect materials cost by 10% or more; 42.86% want to reduce it by 5% or more
  - Here, again, is the purchasing disconnect with the needs of a reliable plant. If purchasing practices are measured by price alone, total cost recovery can suffer.
- 56.67% of the purchasing systems are not part of, or integrated with, a computerized maintenance management system (CMMS)
  - Note: This supports the fact that MRO, as a small part of total spend, is not a factor in a company's purchasing system. It shows the disconnect with purchasing's directive and the maintenance of the CMMS.
- 51.58% responded that purchasing and maintenance do not work together to identify opportunities to substitute or reverse engineer spares and components
  - Note: A major contribution to reducing TCO is realizing the values that can accrue from reengineering and commercializing existing stock keeping units (SKUs)

## NOTABLE OPERATIONS DATA FROM THE STOREROOM SOLUTIONS, INC. STUDY

- 43.44% store parts often to very frequently outside of the designated storeroom in unsecured locations
- 47.54% do not have a point-of-use strategy
- 23.77% do not use a process to identify and manage indirect materials, like disciplined cycle counting and cost-saving initiatives

- 51.64% do not consistently have a maintenance planning system to ensure availability of repair parts
- 56.56% do not consistently have supplies and parts kitted and delivered prior to the technician's arrival for scheduled maintenance events
- 35.25% do not have a consistent plant performance strategy incorporating planned maintenance
- 62.30% of MRO storerooms do not consistently participate in the plant's OpEx strategy
- 42.54% rarely or never utilize barcoding, radio frequency identification (RFID), point-of-use vending and other technologies to control MRO/indirect materials consumption
- 69.06% do not have warranty tracking and cost recovery in their current systems
- 31.49% cannot track the usage of MRO/indirect material parts and their likely lifecycle
- 66.85% have a formal CMMS that is underutilized
- 15.47% do not have a CMMS that is visible to all company locations

# THE BARRIERS TO ACHIEVING OPTIMUM COST REDUCTION

*"The procedures followed by the members of the MRO supply chain, including MRO stores, contribute to the increased total cost of MRO at point of consumption…and are targets for change."*
– A. Hogan, CEO,
Merchants Metals, Inc.

## THE MANUFACTURER

Manufacturers of MRO parts who decide to sell their products via distribution have one or more discount schedules based on their costs and what the market will bear. Some manufacturers will sell directly to the user when the user consumes large quantities and can take large amounts.

Manufacturers have various policies regarding distribution. Some will sell to any distributor who has a standard industrial classification (SIC) code. Some try to limit distribution geographically, but will sell to a given distributor if directed to do so by a significant user. These policies vary in application and time. The most strident are manufacturers who underwrite the distributor's inventory, protect territory and threaten to cancel a distributor if their rules are violated. When these conditions exist, distributors do not challenge these policies because their profits are protected; the users have few competitive options.

A manufacturer sells via a distributor because it is too costly to sell to all possible users directly (i.e., assume the cost of distribution). Although the manufacturer presents a positive, friendly face to its traditional distributors, experience shows the manufacturer basically does not believe distributors earn their discounts or stock enough and pretty much resents the fact that most distributors sell competitive brands. This causes the manufacturer's representative to compete with the distributor's time, which adds to the barriers of distrust, apathy and lack of cooperation, all of which add cost to the MRO supply chain.

## THE DISTRIBUTOR

MRO distributors range from specialty distributors (e.g., safety only, welding only, etc.) to full line distributors who try to sell as many lines and brands as they can.

Some distributors have multi-level distribution centers. For example, a power transmission distributor has five regional warehouses serving over five hundred local distribution points which, in turn, deliver to customers' receiving docks. Additionally, distributors will purchase from other noncompete distributors to obtain brands requested by their customers.

Distributors maintain various costs, including:

➢ Bricks and mortar;

➢ Inventory;

➢ Heat, light, power;

➢ Management;

➢ Inside sales;

➢ Outside sales;

➢ Profit. Profit is included in the supplier's price to their clients, so it is an added cost to the buyer.

Branch managers get paid based on inventory turns, markup terms, personnel and lack of bad debt. Therefore, the manager wants to increase markup wherever possible, reduce the branch's inventory to increase turn rates and rely on manufacturers' inventory to service customers. Managers get a bonus when they take an order with higher markups. This is mostly accomplished on spot buys and unquoted parts. Inside sales and operations personnel think outside sales is all glory with expenses paid while inside people do all the work. Operations feels the outside work is not worth eight percent…the cost of outside sales.

The outside salesperson is faced with hard negotiations from the prospect and an inside force that wants increased markups. Outside sales personnel want more inventory backup to increase service and a lower price to get the order. Generally, they all feel the manufacturer does not do enough to support the distribution function.

The barrier between the manufacturer and distributor is augmented by the multiple barriers within the distributor's organization. These barriers and the duplicated functions, locations, inventories and markups add to the cost of the MRO supply chain.

## THE MRO CONSUMER

There are many and varied objective and subjective barriers that exist where MRO storerooms distribute parts to plant personnel who consume them.

*First…The User*

- ➢ Wants parts on hand when needed
- ➢ Wants specific brands with no substitutions (can cause substitutions to fail)
- ➢ Blames downtime on lack of storeroom service, purchasing, etc.
- ➢ Requests higher inventory with increased min/max level
- ➢ Wants new parts added without commitment to usage
- ➢ Hoards parts in substocks due to perceived lack of storeroom service
- ➢ Enjoys going to the market to prove they can buy cheaper than purchasing
- ➢ Likes to go for pickups
- ➢ Welcomes visits from suppliers
- ➢ Has pressure to complete jobs on time

*Next… The MRO Store Manager Has:*

➢ Limited authority for min/max ordering

➢ Pressure to reduce inventory

➢ Heat for out of stock situations

➢ Limited ability to substitute parts

➢ No money allocation to improve stores' operation systems

*Then… The Budget Holders*

➢ Authorize spot buys and withdrawals from inventory

➢ Ask users to do more with less

➢ Want to eliminate substocks

➢ Have pressure to reduce budget dollars

➢ Want more inventory dollars to increase service

➢ Think their people can do a better job than purchasing

➢ Have little respect for corporate price agreements

*Next… Purchasing*

➢ Puts constant pressure on distributors for lower prices (this adds to the pressure between outside sales and distributor management)

➢ Wants competitive deals, best/lowest pricing

➢ Wants longer terms

➢ Is pressured to get lower prices with smaller quantities

➢ Is pressured to reduce inventories

➢ Is required to show year after year improvements

➢ Wants budget holders to utilize national price agreements

*Lastly… The CFO and Plant Manager*

➢ View the MRO stores' operations as a necessary cost that is not recovered in the manufacturing process

➢ Require lower costs, lower inventory and head count reduction

➢ Want service levels that cause zero downtime

➢ Will not allocate funds to improve stores

Everyone in a plant is involved in MRO in some way. The various job descriptions cause conflicts among departments, creating more barriers to optimum cost reductions and process improvements.

Barriers and duplications add considerable cost to the parts when they finally are consumed in the plant. By defining the duplications from the manufacturer, through distribution, through the internal process and finally to the user, a scenario can be constructed to eliminate the unnecessary steps. Similarly, by recognizing the barriers and getting cooperation among competing functions within the chain, an optimum process can be achieved.

By eliminating the duplicated steps and knocking down the barriers, the optimum cost situation is achieved by placing a qualified provider on-site with a defined process that measures performance to achieve the goals.

To eliminate the barriers and recover storeroom costs, these ingredients are necessary to select a successful on-site MRO provider and attain a reliable MRO operation. Your provider must have:

➢ On-Site Clients as a Sole Source of Revenue – On-site operations should be the provider's sole revenue source. There should be no traditional off-site inventory and no traditional distributor sales. This ensures focus and expertise, and duplicated costs are recovered.

➢ Purchasing Power – Where does the provider stand in the supply chain for all products in your storeroom? Is the provider willing to share all costs net of rebates?

➢ Experience – Can the provider show the benefits of a wide range of experience to ensure a proper path to reach your goals?

➢ Trained Personnel – What are the provider's sources of personnel? How do they get trained and experienced?

➢ Ability to Demonstrate Successful Operations – What are the provider's success stories? What are the pitfalls?

➢ Total Corporation Dedication – Does all management, from the chairperson on down, endorse the on-site concept and are they willing to commit corporate assets to the success of your program? Are corporate assets funneled to other revenue sources?

➢ Compatible Computer Systems – It is necessary to have systems that are unique and dedicated to the distributor's on-site operation. Traditional MRO systems do not have the information units necessary for control.

➢ Ability to Personalize the Operation to Each Plant's Goals – Every plant is different, even those within a corporation. There is no standard approach to achieving the goals. Your provider must recognize differences and be able to adjust implementation and operations to the dynamic needs of each site.

# MRO INSIGHTS

## DO YOU HAVE A "PERFECT STORM" ROOM RATHER THAN A PERFECT STOREROOM?

MRO represents the highest percentage rate of cost recovery available to plant operations, reaching twenty-five to thirty percent. Dilatory situations exist because questions remain unanswered: "Is it worth it?" "What do we achieve?" "Who will do it?" "How is it measured?"

Management does not recognize that a world-class storeroom would improve production and contribute to a site's net profits. Management does not invest the money to improve the situation because of the perception that "MRO is MRO and, therefore, a necessary evil that is not worth improving, even if we could."

When compared to the expertise that companies have applied to their core competencies, MRO is at the nadir since companies are not sure how to improve the situation. They surely do not know how to measure the values that can be released or what they are, hence, inaction.

Sometimes, it takes a near catastrophic situation to get attention to MRO. As an example, the plant manager of a major milk processor was auditing production one Saturday when a foreman exclaimed that there was a leak in one of the processing machines. No one in the plant could find the needed part to stop the leak, so the plant manager went to the storeroom to find the necessary part (at least he knew what to do!). After two hours of searching, a part was found and installed. Okay? No, not okay! The description for the part did not match the actual part and the wrong part was installed, making the situation worse. Milk spewed, instead of leaking, production was shut down and frustration reigned. As a result of the near catastrophe, which also affected bonuses, the company invested in a reengineering effort for the storeroom that included proper naming, locations, bar code control and security. In other words, the company achieved world-class storeroom status by contracting with a third-party on-site MRO management company.

Lessons learned? The costly loss of production could have been avoided if the company had recognized the potential disaster inherent in a "perfect storm room" and acted before the disaster occurred. When disaster seems evident, some companies will strive for what they call a perfect storeroom. Is there a logical answer to this dilemma? Does a world-class storeroom status exist that would have most of the attributes of a "perfect storeroom" and still achieve a desirable return on investment (ROI) scenario?

To go from "storm room" to "world-class" status is attainable from an ROI standpoint because the cost of world-class is paid out of the savings that accrue. To go from "world-class" to "perfect" does not have economies of scale. The added benefits are not worth the additional cost, therefore, the optimum situation is world-class status. This only can be achieved from an expert on-site provider that has world-class MRO capabilities as its core competency and total operational focus.

Companies cannot do "IT" themselves or they would have done so already. The excuses vary from don't know how to don't have the time to don't have the personnel. They cannot because of their position in the MRO supply chain (i.e., no functional discount) and because they will not apply budget dollars to the effort.

The traditional distributor does not achieve world-class status for the company because of franchise restrictions, lack of original equipment manufacturer (OEM) relationships and the existence of multiple marketing foci, only one of which may be knowledge of how to provide world-class status for its customers. Moreover, the traditional distributor does not achieve world-class status for its customers because its functions represent a costly duplication in the supply chain that requires fifteen to eighteen percent additional selling, general and administrative (SG&A) expenses to the delivered price of parts. In addition, distributors make more profit with traditional distribution, therefore, they do not want to proactively offer an on-site world-class status program.

**Table 2.1** – Comparison of "Storm Room" vs. "World-Class Storeroom" vs. "Perfect Storeroom."

| ACTIVITY | THE "STORM" ROOM | WORLD-CLASS STOREROOM (WCS) STATUS | THE PERFECT STOREROOM |
|---|---|---|---|
| Availability of Parts | <80% | 98%++ | 100% |
| Spot Buy Control | Little control | Total control | Total control |
| Substock Activity and Control | Increased activity; Little control | Decreased | Eliminated; Total control |
| Excess Inventory; Stock Turn | < One | > Six | > Twelve |
| Inventory Reduction | Increasing | 45% | 60% |
| Obsolescence Recovery | None | 50%-75% | 100% |
| Measured, Controlled Prices | Little on SKUs; None on spot buys | Total control | Total control |
| Inventory Accuracy | 85% at max | 99%++ | 100% |
| Transaction Burden | 15,000 per $1.0MM in spend | 24/year regardless of spend | 24/year regardless of spend |
| Audit Trail Control | Questionable | Unassailable | Unassailable |
| Corporate Contract Compliance | Can be circumvented | 100% compliance | 100% compliance |
| Warranties Exercised | Not exercised | 100% utilized | 100% utilized |
| Information Flow | Lacking or nonexistent | Web-based visibility of all functions | Web-based visibility of all functions |
| Stakeholder Satisfaction | Not satisfied | Reasonably satisfied | 100% satisfied |
| Unauthorized Issues; Communication | Excessive; Little communication | Recovery exercised; Controlled | Eliminated |
| Safety | Questionable compliance | 100% compliance | 100% compliance |
| Inventory Duplications | Excessive | Eliminated | Eliminated |
| Definition of Spend and Inventory Levels | Not known; Inaccurate estimates | 100% defined | 100% defined |
| Downtime due to Stock outs; Emergencies | Unavoidable; Not measured | Minimized/resolved | Zero downtime |
| Productivity | Not recognized; Not implemented; Not measured | Continual productivity programs effected with measurement | 100% capture of all productivity opportunities |

**Figure 2.1:** Comparison: An existing "Storm Room" cost drain to benefits from world-class storeroom investment vs. a perfect storeroom's R.O.I.

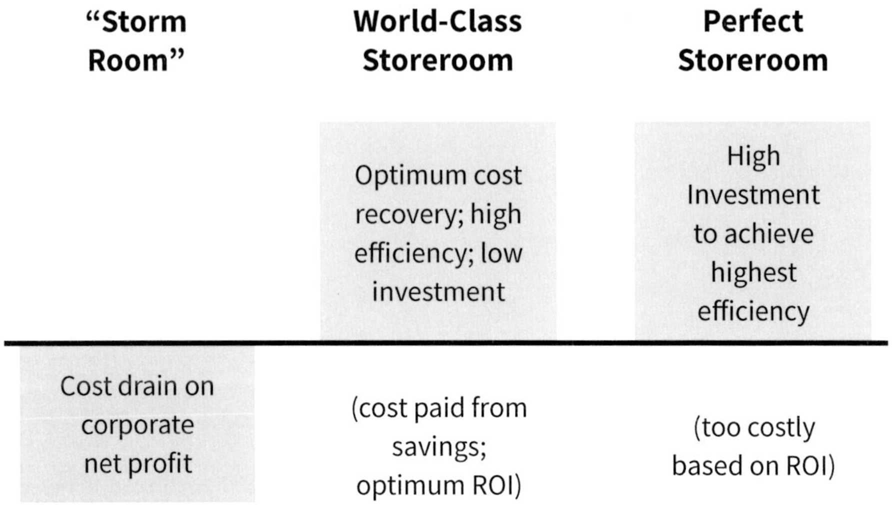

| "Storm Room" | World-Class Storeroom | Perfect Storeroom |
|---|---|---|
| | Optimum cost recovery; high efficiency; low investment | High Investment to achieve highest efficiency |
| Cost drain on corporate net profit | (cost paid from savings; optimum ROI) | (too costly based on ROI) |

## WHY DOES THE CONDITION CONTINUE TO EXIST?

Companies are not willing to invest the dollars necessary to achieve the perfect storeroom; it is too expensive and they lack the expertise to implement and maintain such an operation. The perceived value effected by the perfect storeroom will not be supported by finance, therefore, the situation continues with blame for stock outs, downtime, worker inefficiencies, purchasing not buying enough quickly enough, poor stock-keeping unit (SKU) management (e.g., did not adjust min/max, etc.) and engineering (e.g., poor planning).

Each of the three plant stakeholders has a different agenda. The engineers and plant personnel want the perfect storeroom. Finance wants less investment of dollars, as well as a reduction of the administrative burden, and the plant manager wants productivity and profit with no downtime.

## WHAT IS THE ANSWER

The answer lies in empowerment of experts who can deliver what is needed to provide this world-class status. The expert selected should have a single focus of on-site storeroom management, show a history of success and demonstrate the ability to produce and measure value. When these experts bring their expertise on-site, the existing "storm" room vanishes. By empowering the experts, companies achieve world-class status with an optimum return on investment.

# BAD DESCRIPTIONS, BAD DECISIONS, HIGH COSTS

The world of MRO is replete with pitfalls, errors and uncontrolled costs (not just price). An example is the condition of descriptions. It is rare that a company's SKU listing has complete descriptions because most are missing one or more important attributes. With inadequate SKU descriptions, the company is open to quote and shipment responses that can cause disruptions to plant operations.

For example, an RFQ for fuses has the brand and the amps, but the volts and part numbers are missing. The supplier will quote the price of the fuse with the lowest volts because it is the cheapest. If the supplier is awarded the business and then is told the fuses are wrong (i.e., the higher voltage is required), the price goes up. It is now too late to switch suppliers.

The same thing occurs when a brand is not specified. The lowest price is quoted, only to find out that only one certain brand is acceptable. Again, it is too late to change.

Many RFQs do not include quantities or consistent units of measure. A supplier can quote an assumption of order quantity and then raise the price when order quantities are small or contain an amount where a package has to be broken open. When the unit of measure for ordering is different than the unit of issue, the quantities on the RFQ can be misleading and cause inconsistent price quotes. The effect of inadequate information is a potentially dangerous situation in which savings are lost and/or inadequate parts are used.

In every scenario where MRO improvements become recognized as critical for reliability, data cleansing is critical to success. SKU descriptions must be established with nouns, attributes and units of measure that clearly describe each SKU. What's more, this data must be consistent among all SKUs in all storerooms throughout an organization.

# CRITICAL SPARES

Spare parts management can be a contributor to reliability or a serious drag on a company's ability to meet delivery schedules.

In too many cases, an unreliable and unresponsive MRO storeroom can cause maintenance engineers to draw out large quantities of critical SKUs to stash in uncontrolled locations throughout the facility. These requisitioners should not be blamed; they are guarding against a lack of supply that could cause downtime for which they are blamed. Therefore, the lack of reliability on the part of MRO management is the cause of duplicated inventory. Remember, dollars in substock have value, so they are considered inventory.

This situation also causes out of stock situations for other requisitions and, in turn, costly emergency actions for purchasing, logistics and the suppliers.

## SPARE PARTS DECISION GUIDE

**Spare Parts:** Are they a help or a hindrance to mean time to repair (MTTR)? Ask yourself:

> ➤ Is your spare parts storeroom reliable?
>
> ➤ Is your storeroom a candidate for improvement?

The spare parts decision guide is designed to alert you to the potential dangers and unnecessary costs that exist from the unreliable supply of critical parts. The guide should provide an impetus for change.

If you answer "YES" or "I DON'T KNOW" to 50% or more of the following questions, your stores operation is a hindrance to MTTR and contains waste (MUDA) that should be eliminated.

| YES | I DON'T KNOW | |
|-----|--------------|---|
| | | Does downtime exist because of stock outs? |
| | | Are inventory counts inaccurate? |
| | | Are maintenance personnel required to spend time on stores' operations? |
| | | Is the same part stocked under different stock numbers? |
| | | Do multiple locations within your storeroom contain the same items? |
| | | Do uncontrolled substocks exist in using departments? |
| | | Are 10 percent or more of the SKUs obsolete? |
| | | Are emergency orders significant? |
| | | Does management require inventory reductions? |
| | | Does the inventory in your MRO storeroom turn less than two times per year? |
| | | Does MRO inventory exceed the amount of replacement spend? |
| | | Do suppliers invoice for each shipment? |
| | | Is there a need to reduce transactions? |
| | | Do you have more than fifty MRO suppliers? |
| | % | TOTAL |

Reliable storerooms require "YES" answers to the following questions. If you answer "NO" to any of these questions, spare parts availability is unreliable and requires restructuring.

| YES | NO | |
|-----|-----|---|
| | | Is stores' management coordinated with reliable maintenance programs? |
| | | Do stores maintain bill of materials (BOM) and master equipment list (MEL) data? |
| | | Does stores' management participate in scheduled maintenance meetings? |
| | | Is stores' management authorized to change order quantities/minimal/maximum levels? |
| | | Is there management recognition that spares availability is critical to mean time to repair (MTTR)? |
| | | Is there general agreement that MRO needs redesign? |
| | | Do all maintenance teams have the correct parts when needed? |

## DANGER SIGNALS

Here are the six main danger signals that are detrimental to production reliability. They are not listed in order of severity because they are all severe.

1. A critical spare is removed from stores during off hours and not recorded.
2. Your CFO looks at MRO inventory and sees an opportunity to recover cash.
3. There is little attention to usage fluctuations vs. min/max reorder activity.
4. Descriptions of parts are inadequate; parts in inventory are duplicated and exist under various SKU numbers.
5. Parts are taken in quantities that are not immediately needed, causing stock outs for use in other departments.
6. Functions are added for stores to perform without recognition of priority, expertise, or time to execute.

# RELIABILITY

## SPARE PARTS AND YOUR MTTR, MTBR AND FMEA

A reliable product is defined as an item that is purchased more than once by the consumer or by industry. A reliable product requires a reliable plant which, in turn, requires reliable assets.

The maintenance mantra is to keep the plant running efficiently with zero downtime. When an asset goes down, analysis is performed utilizing mean time to repair (MTTR), mean time between repair (MTBR), or failure mode and effects analysis (FMEA) techniques. But all of these actions are implemented after the fact. In other words, they answer the question, "What happened?" Solutions should be anticipated/identified AND applied before a situation develops to avoid the downtime.

Responsibility for critical spares comes under the management of the MRO storeroom. What are critical spares? By definition, it is any SKU that, when missing, may result in production downtime. It may elongate MTTR when the required part is out of stock and needs to be ordered as an emergency, causing increases in transportation and freight, price and employee opportunity costs let alone the cost of non-production.

Critical spares also include any missing SKU that causes maintenance personnel to lose time in achieving department goals. Therefore, the goal of managing the MRO storeroom must be aligned with the goal of maintenance reliability and avoid elongating MTTR and MTBR before the fact. Stores should collect data on FMEA, adjust inventory accordingly and report to maintenance.

A reliable supply of spare parts requires employing a number of available techniques to reach reliability goals. These include reengineering, commercialization, supplier support, maintenance communications and deep/uniform descriptions of every active SKU in the storeroom. In addition, senior management must recognize the role that the unreliable storeroom plays in deflating plant profitability. Management must invest in the steps necessary to elevate stores' operations to the level required to support a reliable plant.

MRO needs kaizen events to achieve change for the better! Adding a function to MRO operations requiring coordination with maintenance reliability programs would be a kaizen event.

# WHY IS MRO IGNORED?

Some pundits have stated that MRO parts can be up to fifty percent or more of a company's maintenance budget, therefore, MRO is an important area of consideration. But, if it is that important, why is MRO generally ignored when cost improvement opportunities are considered? There are three main reasons:

1. Lack of knowledge of how to initiate, operate and sustain a world-class stores operation.

2. Lack of management recognition and financial support to facilitate change (i.e., it's only MRO, put up with it).

3. Lack of time to plan, propose and gain approval to change due to daily time commitments and emergencies, many of which are caused by an unreliable storeroom in the first place.

As a result, the MRO enigma remains in a static environment and continues to be a detriment to plan reliability. Generally, corporate procurement personnel are not focused on MRO's total cost because their performance is mainly or totally measured on reducing the price paid for any target commodity. In general, companies believe that managing indirect materials is too impractical based on marginal ROI and too costly to be worth the time spent. Procurement is tasked to attack the top opportunities. They are told: "Concentrate on direct materials, which are ninety percent of our spend, and let MRO costs be the plant's problem."

Proper management for MRO stores requires knowledge, skill and time to achieve world-class reliability. Plants rarely have the skill sets or the time to effectively negotiate an optimum MRO agreement, let alone implement it properly. Purchasing is directed to the large spend opportunity, therefore, MRO change is sporadic and lacking.

# CONNECTING MRO STORES TO RELIABLE MAINTENANCE

Achieving optimum maintenance reliability depends on myriad factors in the process of delivering a reliable plant. The existence of an uncontrolled and/or unconnected MRO stores operation represents a significant deterrent to the success of maintenance reliability goals and to the delivery of a reliable plant. The existence of diverse influences on the MRO storeroom contributes to the restraints affecting maintenance reliability.

## WHAT ARE THESE INFLUENCES?

- Finance is looking to reduce inventory and recover cash flow ( ergo, buy less; use what you have).
- Purchasing is charged with paying less while buying less.
- Engineering is tasked with continually improving operations and aggressively recommending state-of-the-art procedures that entail new equipment, equipment upgrades and lean objectives. These functions require the pur-

chase of new SKUs and impact obsolescence. Therefore, engineering is adding inventory and reducing usage.

- Maintenance requirements include having the correct parts in the quantities needed and on time. Under the present MRO situation, this results in requests for more inventory and more SKUs (i.e., more investment). Maintenance professionals cannot realize all the benefits available from their investment in reliable maintenance concepts unless the goals, functions and management of MRO stores are structured and sustained to support the ongoing goals of maintenance reliability.

## WHAT ARE THE RESTRAINTS?

Finance, procurement, engineering and plant maintenance all have their directed duties and all report activities and results to the plant manager. The responsibility for delivering a reliable product at a profit lies with the plant manager, who is dependent on the performance results delivered by the senior staff.

These disciplines are designed to work as a team connected to a smoothly functioning operation producing reliable products. When it comes to MRO stores' operations, "smoothly functioning" does not exist because each discipline has diverse and conflicting job directives surrounding the traditional MRO world.

*"The cost of MRO storeroom operations are not recovered in the manufacturing process and constitute a drain on plant profitability."*
– Ralph Bolton, Author, "Systems Contracting"

# MAINTENANCE AND YOUR MRO STOREROOM – COORDINATED VS. UNCOORDINATED

Here is a comparison of storerooms showing the difference between an MRO storeroom that is coordinated with maintenance programs and one that is uncoordinated.

| MAINTENANCE RELIABILITY/ LEAN OBJECTIVES | TYPICAL COMPANY-OWNED MRO STORES UNCOORDINATED |
|---|---|
| • Eliminate MUDA (waste)<br>• Create MEL (Master Equipment List)<br>• Apply reliability-centered maintenance (RCM)<br>• Recognize FMEA<br>• Proactive root cause failure analysis (RCFA) | • Low priority<br>• People marking time<br>• Little MRO parts strategy; no improvement incentive<br>• Discouraged supplier productivity<br>• Unconnected to maintenance<br>• Managed and/or directed by diverse disciplines<br>• Unreliable service<br>• Uncontrolled duplications; substocks |
| **GOALS** | **GOALS** |
| • Effect planned quality production<br>• Provide lowest cost; preserve integrity<br>• Deliver a reliable plant | • Reduce inventory<br>• Reduce price<br>• Reduce personnel costs<br>• Recover substocks<br>• Discourage supplier in-plant activities<br>• Cut paperwork |

# MAINTENANCE AND YOUR MRO STORE-ROOM COORDINATED

| MAINTENANCE RELIABILITY/ LEAN OBJECTIVES | WORLD-CLASS STORES MANAGEMENT COORDINATED TO OBJECTIVES |
|---|---|
| • Eliminate MUDA<br>• Create MEL<br>• Apply RCM<br>• Recognize FMEA<br>• Proactive RCFA | • MUDA – Eliminate waste; duplication of SKUs; duplication of processes<br>• MEL – SKUs reflect MEL detail min/max<br>• RCM – Parts on hand in quantity needed<br>• FMEA – Be prepared; communication; history<br>• RCFA – Participate in preventive drills; take action |
| **GOALS**<br><br>• Effect planned quality production<br>• Provide lowest cost; preserve integrity<br>• Deliver a reliable plant | **GOALS / BENEFITS COORDINATED**<br><br>• Right size inventory to MEL min/max<br>• Optimize price/productivity<br>• Participate/contribute to objectives<br>• Measure and report financial and non-financial benefits via key performance indicators (KPIs)<br>• Deliver a reliable storeroom operation/improve<br>• Recover personnel time, downtime, lost production<br>• Costs paid from savings |

# REASONS FOR MRO STATUS QUO: THE MAINTENANCE DEPARTMENT

Here are some factors that contribute to inaction by maintenance personnel:

- Stores responsibility assigned as an adjunct with no job assignment.
- Change resistance: "This is how we have always done it."
- Fear of the unknown: "If I agree to change and it fails, will I have egg on my face?"
- Favored suppliers: "Been with us for 25 years."
- Personnel: Placeholder for short-term, limited ability associates.
- Knowledge: "What would we change to?" "How would we do it?" "With whom?"
- Timing / Priority: "When is there time to plan/execute change?"
- Financial: No dollars for MRO improvement; no budget assignment.
- Resignation: **"It is what it is; put up with it."**

There are times when stores' operations cause serious downtime and negate production goals. This is when corrective measures are attempted. The extent of these actions is based on how severe the MRO failures are in causing downtime and effecting negative production numbers. Consultants are hired who set forth corrective procedures. MRO "naming" companies are engaged to enhance descriptions and dot.com companies are invited to improve the process. At best, these procedures improve the existing service level to an acceptable level. The consultants and others set forth procedures that will help solve the MRO problem, but they do not do it. They teach, but they do not sustain. The improvements never reach optimum because of an MRO culture that does not recognize the financial and non-financial costs that MRO stores inflict on plant profitability. As a result, MRO is not included as a major factor in the plant improvement process.

It is a proven fact that when MRO improvement programs are implemented by the company, the benefits are short-lived and not sustained. It matters not which discipline institutes the improvements, sustainability is not maintained because MRO stores' operations are not a sole function assigned to a management professional. Rather, the MRO management function is assigned to individuals who maintain job descriptions with much higher priorities. This is the main reason why companies cannot obtain all the potential value that can be realized from the MRO process.

Maintenance professionals will not "put up with it," will not allow the vagaries of poor MRO stores' service to defeat their mantra to provide a reliable plant. In the real world, maintenance professionals will protect their own projects by utilizing methods to make sure they have the critical spares they need when they want them in the quantity necessary to complete their mission. These methods include:

- Building of uncontrolled substocks;
- Adding SKUs with descriptions known only to the requester;
- Increasing min/max quantities;
- Buying around MRO stores and corporate agreements;
- Engaging suppliers to "hold" special inventory.

All these activities are deemed necessary by maintenance professionals to protect their projects when the MRO store is unreliable. At the same time, these necessities constitute additional, unmeasured costs that impact plant profitability.

Now enter corporate policies, which are geared toward controlling and improving corporate performance for the stockholders. Applying generic principles are safe and proven methods for the corporation; they provide a safe haven for practitioners, but do not recognize the nuances inherent in the MRO world. Here is an example: The Corporation requires ANY contract worth over $20MM to go out on quote and dictates a reverse auction or other methods that negotiate best buy practices. This may be fine for all things, but **not** for MRO operations. Under these conditions, the MRO contract is awarded to the low price bidder while assuming all the complex operational requirements will be met. Corporate directs the plant to use the tools provided, such as systems, applications and products (SAP) type systems and corporate-assigned supply base with the agreed pricing (i.e., market baskets).

Here is where MRO differs. The assigned suppliers have only priced less than ten percent of historical MRO spend as opposed to all other bid projects where all usage/services are clearly defined and identified. MRO spot buys are not contained in corporate agreements, another contribution to the uncontrolled and unconnected MRO storeroom. The assigned supplier is chosen via a low bid on less than ten percent of the historical spend, while spot buys, at thirty to forty percent of spend, remain uncontrolled, resulting in more contributions to MRO unreliability.

How can MRO operations be connected to reliable maintenance programs and still provide an optimum cost position for the plant? THE PLANT CANNOT DO IT THEMSELVES.

The answer is a customized third-party MRO (3PMRO) contract with a provider that has stores' management as its core revenue source with a focus and commitment to total on-site MRO stores management. The deliverables must be measured with KPIs indigenous to the needs of each plant. On-site personnel must be trained and experienced in stores' management techniques *and* be conversant with maintenance reliability objectives, such as FMEA, RCFA, etc. To be successful and sustainable, moving to 3PMRO cannot include traditional supplier selection techniques. The selection process should proceed as follows:

1. Pick your provider based on focus, experience, record of success and top-down corporate commitment to your MRO goals.

2. Write the site operating agreement in concert with financials, KPIs, guarantees and implementation requirements.

3. Obtain agreement from all disciplines.

4. Implement and start on time because your first step will determine your future.

5. Measure and report.

The impact of a properly implemented and controlled 3PMRO program that is connected to your maintenance reliability enterprises will have a profound positive effect on providing reliable equipment and, as a result, a reliable plant producing reliable products.

# THE RFQ PROCESS

*"The widely used request-for-quote or request-for-proposal (RFQ/RFP) methods to select MRO suppliers represent a dysfunctional process that results in trite, confused and sometimes spurious responses. Too many times, the fallacies of the system force the requester to select subjectively and/or stay with the same supply base. The cost of the process can exceed the real value produced, especially if a consultant is involved, and measurements of benefits vs. promises are cloudy and unreal."*

– George Krauter (that would be me)

Responsible members of the supply chain continue spending money on committees, consultants and others to go out on quote so they can show senior management that the selected supplier and the selected process is the best the market has to offer. In fact, the cost of the entire quote process can exceed the real value received, even when the value is measured accurately, which is rarely the case.

Most in the supply chain recognizes, albeit internally, the fallacy of the present process, but no one overtly objects because they cannot conceive a better alternative that would improve the process. At best, senior management seems to be satisfied that this method of quoting is the best method available, so why stir unnecessary trouble while entertaining fear of the unknown (i.e., change)?

## THE TYPICAL PROCESS

Let's start at the beginning: Senior management is mildly satisfied with last year's performance of the purchasing department and now wants to know from the vice president of purchasing: "What are you going to do for me this year?" The vice president looks at all areas of available cost reductions and zeros in on the arcane world of MRO. Here is where things start to go wrong.

The vice president asks the managers for unrealistic cost reduction goals (does the VP mean cost or price?), which leads the managers to say; "Sure, we can do that." They now go back to their departments and wonder how they can do that. Incidentally, what happens when you, as a purchasing vice president, agree to and/or think you can get a fifteen percent price reduction? Are you admitting that there was more there last year and you did not get it? You have to be ready with smoke and mirrors to answer that one.

The managers are in the middle. The boss has agreed to unreachable goals, they face a lukewarm supplier base (here they come again after what we gave them last year) and a set of requisitioners who have little tolerance for change (the line is down because of the cheap supplier you chose). Although during the RFQ process the managers espouse that price is only part of the consideration, in the real world, price is the overwhelming measurement for which the program is valued. Just how difficult is it to explain to a budget holder that a higher price was paid to an alternative supplier because of other values produced? In addition, it is rare that managers truly understand the real drivers of the MRO supply chain and can take action to produce benefits other than price control.

Okay purchasing manager, it's time to go out on quote. First, form a cross-functional committee so you can spread the responsibility. This is when costs begin to occur and no one thinks to measure the cost of the project itself. Committee members have many other agendas they consider far more important than having more meetings. The purchasing manager also has more important things pressing (remember, MRO is just ten percent of the total purchase; what about the other ninety percent?). Therefore, an MRO request coordinator, usually an assistant manager, is assigned with the responsibility of managing and scheduling the process. Now this assistant manager also has other duties, which adds to the opportunity costs incurred by the creation of the committee. But, there is still no measurement of the cost.

The assistant manager probably has little experience in MRO proposals and is either directed by a senior manager or goes to the files and duplicates the last RFQ with updated goal requirements. In addition, any newRFQ in today's market adds questions about capabilities regarding integrated supply (whatever that is) and e-commerce, which elicits more confusion.

Now the RFQ timing schedule is set and spread out over four months (in reality, it can expand to six or eight months). The schedule includes dates for meetings, mailings, walk-throughs, responses, meetings, phone calls, meetings and a starting date. Intertwined in this time span are multiple subjective pressures from incumbents, friends of the CEO and anyone else who wants to get into the act. Finally, the committee has an approved RFQ and an approved supplier list that grows as if it had its own life. The big questions for the committee are whether to:

- Include a market basket price quote in the RFQ;
- Leave prices to later and send a request for proposal;
- Send a request for information (RFI);
- Send some of the other request for scenarios.

The lack of pricing in the initial request will add more steps (i.e., costs) because price is king under the present system.

## THE PRICING

An important part of pricing is the market basket. If more than five hundred SKUs are requested, responses are sporadic and unwieldy. Good quoting practices suggest that parts be selected from high, medium and low usage items, but little attention is paid to this. Quoted parts are selected from inventory SKUs because of historic data availability, which is sometimes inaccurate. Fifty percent of parts consumed are non-stock items. These onetime buys have no basis for comparison, in other words, no history and no price data versus timing factors. Onetime buys are not included in the RFQ and not measured (more on this later). If five hundred SKUs are selected as a pricing sample (max) and the company has ten thousand inventory items, the quote is for five percent of the SKUs. Since fifty percent of the buy consists of onetimers and not included in the quote, the RFP is for two and five tenths percent of the company's total SKU range.

Now, distributors know this and they also know that if their prices are high on the market basket, they will be out of consideration, no matter what other values are presented. Therefore, the process causes distributors to offer lower margin pricing on the quote, which will be made up on the onetimers, because it can. In addition, distributors will quote lowest brand cost. If challenged after selection is made, they can either sell the lower brand or plead ignorance, knowing it is too late for the company to change. Other problems include unit of measure, timing of prices in the database and brand differences between what is on the shelf versus what is described in the SKU. Let's not forget that the process takes six to eight months, during which market prices change (real world or imagined), which, in turn, allows the chosen supplier to vacillate prices charged versus the market basket quote.

Considering these facts, market baskets have no objective value and, in fact, deter from proper decision-making. Nevertheless, market baskets continue to be a part of the quote process with little thought given to alternatives. Due to many factors, including the unpredictable nature of MRO and lack of stock turn, unit prices quoted rarely can be applied to actual contract pricing and be measured accurately. Price arrangements for non-quoted parts that include cost-plus (will you audit?) and discounts from list price sheets are impossible to administrate (try to track that with ten thousand SKUs and multiple discounts by product and by market).

Consider this: All MRO quotes go to distributors. Manufacturers set the price for distributors, who then add margin and set prices to make a profit. Squeezing distributors for price affects how much priority distributors give a program in terms of delivery and other services. The MRO manufacturer's goal is to have its products as standard use in the user's plant. Manufacturers spend considerable dollars on product engineers who call on product decision-makers to get the manufacturer's brand specified. This is called pulling the product through distribution. However, the MRO manufacturer has a hazard here in that, although it can be successful in getting brands specified in the plant, the order goes to a distributor who may switch brands based on stock, margins and a competitive price necessary to get the order. Effective price negotiation must employ the manufacturer, as well as the distributor, to gain the best possible continuing price situation.

## THE SUPPLIERS

As a potential supplier, you receive the RFQ and are likely to think, "They're out on quote again… moans and groans…time too short…whose account is it…who will respond…how? You go to your RFQ library and enter all the paragraphs that fit; sometimes close enough is okay. Now, you call the company coordinator with questions that are referred to the committee. If a potential impact exists, answers are given. If a change is made for one supplier, the RFQ must be changed for all. This equals more time and cost. Pricing is given to your purchasing department, which decides whether parts have enough description, which parts will be quoted, which brands can be substituted and what other national pricing agreements can be applied to this quote. Should you include rebates in your cost of goods if a cost-plus clause is requested? If you do not, how will you stand an audit? There are always questions to be answered especially when OEM and/or blueprint parts are included. It begs the question why any company would include them. Asking and obtaining answers extend time and cause scheduling changes.

The RFQ asks you for your ability to cut costs in areas other than price. In other words, what process do you recommend to cut paperwork, inventory, personnel, etc.? Your answer is based on what will get you to the next round of consideration, not what the company should do. How would you know? There is not enough data in the RFQ for a true comprehensive proposal!

Suppliers are asked to come in for a supplier walk-through and other supplier type meetings, which leads to more costs – direct and opportunity. Since all these meetings seem to be the same, with the same questions asked and same answers given, why have them? Suppliers send middle management people who fall into one of these categories: Those who nod off; those who are scared and wonder if they will lose the business; those aggressive newcomers (usually pompous) who aggressively ask numerous questions that have obvious answers to show their acumen and superiority; and those who take away information that dictates their responses, whether they believe it or not. The supplier meetings are an effort by the requester to show "partnership" and willingness to share information, but the information wall still exists. A free flow of critical data to achieve an optimum situation rarely exists. The suppliers attend because they are out if they don't. The cost is high and the return is minimal.

# THE RESPONSES AND THE REQUESTER

Now you are the requester and here comes the responses. You do price first because price rules. When questioned, selecting the low price supplier is safe; you can teach this supplier how to perform if you knew what you needed. Next question: Are all suppliers capable? Of course they are or they would not have been included (except for the loyal, local supplier who is included as a courtesy).

Next dilemma: You asked for the suppliers' ideas on how they would cut all costs; you asked them to respond to specific requirements. All responses are positive, varied and difficult to compare objectively. All have desirable promises and all have missed one or more points deemed necessary for success. How to choose? You asked for references, so you look at them. All suppliers have wonderful references, but you have little time to audit them. The references are all positive, otherwise you would not have received them. So why obtain references? So when asked, you can say, "Oh yes, I checked references, I don't know why the supplier failed." This is another cost with little value.

In this whole process, objective and subjective dynamics are in action. Since objectivity is difficult to measure, subjectivity takes over. Fear of the unknown prevails. Pressure from requisitioners exists and job security could be affected by a wrong supplier/process decision. Let the committee recommend and the VP decide; let's spread the guilt.

Incumbents usually get the nod because they are the safe choice, unless the VP is new, in which case, the incumbent is usually in trouble because new people want new actions. Kind of makes you wonder why you did all this in the first place.

Now, assume the supplier selection is complete and the new agreement is signed, initiated and in operation. Did it work? Was it worth the cost of the quote? How do you know? Can you measure? Why quote? Why change if you cannot measure?

# MEASURING

Measurements are flawed for a number of reasons:

- Savings occur in one area, uncontrolled costs rise in another.
- If the program is driven by purchasing, then the savings come from purchasing's area of responsibility. Costs controlled by other departments may or may not be included. The reverse occurs when the effort is driven by facilities and others.

To measure the full effect of the RFQ, an understanding of the total cost of MRO at point of consumption must exist. Measure each cost factor and you have validity. Companies and suppliers rarely understand the true costs that exist in the MRO supply chain and rarely provide the opportunity to learn, much less do something about it. Since costs are either not understood by chain members or not recognized by the CFO of the consumer, the desired cost reductions are not measured with veracity.

Examples: A CFO of a major chemical company said that inventory reduction had no value to her because the corporation did not charge her profit center with the cost of money. In another situation, inventory recovery was discounted because it was expensed when purchased (IRS where are you?) and, therefore, had no value. If expensed inventory has no value, then everyone should be able to take it home.

Why does the condition continue to exist? It's the "walls" that do it. There is a wall between the requisitioner and purchasing and a wall between purchasing and the distributor's salesperson. A wall exists between the supplier's salespeople and their management and a wall exists between the distributors and the manufacturers they represent. All have agendas and all believe the others do not perform well for the profits they take from the system.

With this kind of situation in the MRO supply chain, there can be little change in the quote response scenarios. To be effective, the walls must come down and all costs and ROI requirements must be shared.

## WHAT HAVE YOU LEARNED?

- Senior management sets unreachable goals and purchasing management agrees to them.
- Market basket quotes cannot be properly measured or applied and could result in the selection of the wrong supplier.
- Suppliers will make promises, both unrealistic and vague, to get to the next levels.
- The RFQ process for MRO material is cost/benefit prohibitive.
- There is a better way to select a supplier base that will satisfy the cost recovery needs of the company and provide adequate ROI for the suppliers.
- If you consider hiring a consultant, take all the costs involved in the present process and apply a multiplier. You will receive a package that is also available at your local library or one that has been utilized for another project.
- If you are an MRO consumer, take the time to know all the real costs that

exist in the supply chain and work to get rid of duplications, no matter which member performs them.

- Get your hands dirty and study parts usage and definitions so measurements can be real and accurate. Establish a process that will work in your plant and require the supplier to perform it. Do not ask the supplier what it will do, tell the supplier what to do, then you must audit…audit…audit. If you are a potential supplier, do the same thing. Instead of responding to a quote by rote, get to know all the prospect's costs and offer a process that will reach its goals while including the sharing of all costs so performance can be audited and measured. You must always be ready to answer the question, "Why in the world did we change to this?"

# INHERENT FLAWS IN THE MARKET BASKET PROCESS

Your CEO is in a cost-cutting frame of mind. MRO is one of the cost reduction projects that purchasing has been assigned to address. The existing MRO situation includes:

➢ Ten thousand parts with assigned SKU numbers;

➢ Many parts with varying brands, stock numbers and descriptions within the same SKU;

➢ The same parts from different manufacturers under different SKU numbers;

➢ No information regarding non-stock/spot buys that constitute thirty-five percent of the value of the spend;

➢ Descriptions of existing SKUs that are inadequate in defining the parts accurately to new suppliers;

➢ Inaccurate predictions of spend due to the very nature of MRO and the effects of excessive inventory versus usage; this is augmented by requisitions and/or purchase orders (POs) that are placed around the storeroom and not recorded as spend dollars;

➢ Unit prices in the system that have not been updated; some exist at .01 cent as placeholders.

On what basis will purchasing be able to select the best, low cost provider and measure the effects for the CEO? The traditional (tried and true?) method is to issue an RFQ that contains a market basket quote. This quote is then analyzed and the low cost supplier is selected. Purchasing can then report to senior management that the purchasing department was able to save the company X% on MRO.

## HERE ARE THE FLAWS

➤ The three major flaws in the process to compare competitive pricing are:

1. Last Price Paid (LPP)
   If quoted prices are compared to last price paid, systems that have not been updated have the price when last purchased, which could be outdated.
   *…price comparisons must be current.*

2. Unit of Measure (UOM)
   A UOM on a SKU could vary based on what is issued versus what is stocked versus what is received versus what is invoiced. For example, fasteners are invoiced per hundred, could be shipped/received in packs of twenty-five and issued by the each.
   *…price comparisons must maintain a consistent UOM.*

3. Brand on RFQ vs. Brand on Shelf
   When the brand on the shelf accepted by the user is different than the brand described in the RFQ, the incumbent has the advantage. For example, a light switch brand specified on the RFQ is an industrial grade, high quality toggle switch. The current supplier has been shipping a household brand that costs forty percent less than the industrial brand. Unsuspecting competitors will quote the specified industrial brand, while the existing supplier will quote the lesser brand and call it the industrial brand.
   *…the brand on the shelf must be the brand on the RFQ.*

➤ With ten thousand SKUs, no one will quote them all, therefore, a sample is put forth on the market basket quote request. Five hundred SKUs are about the maximum reasonable quote request, or just five percent of the SKUs. Suppliers will cut margins on the five percent and make more on non-quoted SKUs and the spot buys not included in the RFQ.

➤ The market basket process is lengthy. The collection of data, assembly of the RFQ/market basket, and selection of a potential supplier list takes time. In addition, the suppliers need at least a month or more to respond and then the analysis and selection process begins, including supplier meetings. Many months pass before a selection is made. With hundreds of manufacturers involved who sell through the potential suppliers selected, discounts and list prices could change, and they do. Now the supplier is chosen and that supplier comes back and wants relief (i.e., a higher price; never lower) because of the price changes. It's too late to requote, so relief is given. The RFQ cost is excessive, especially when the opportunity cost is considered. This cost does not just exist with the RFQ issuing company; it is a cost the suppliers (distributors) must shoulder to prepare, meet and submit.

## SO, WHAT IS THE ANSWER?

How can the purchasing department select the best MRO supplier to satisfy the CEO's request for cost reduction and still satisfy maintenance to get compliance on the agreement?

Here is an agreement that was implemented successfully: First, a supplier was selected based on experience, commitment and a willingness to share all costs. Second, the supplier agreed to a scope of work presented to it by purchasing.

**The Scope:**

1. Pricing: The supplier was told what price the company would pay per SKU; the supplier did not have to quote. The supplier obtained needed margins from its sources of supply. **This satisfied the CEO for cost reduction.**
2. Operations: The supplier established an on-site MRO management process using company employees. KPIs were established, which included:

> ➤ Inventory accuracy;
> ➤ SKU description consistency;
> ➤ Fill rate goals;
> ➤ Inventory and paper processing reductions.

**This satisfied maintenance.**

## CONCLUSION

Purchasing accomplished the goals set by the CEO and still enabled maintenance to perform duties with a reliable MRO operation.

**All were satisfied.**

# THE COST OF PROCESSING THE PURCHASE ORDER CYCLE

In efforts to calculate costs, companies will select cost centers for scrutiny and hire consultants to collect data, draw conclusions and recommend actions for saving potentials.

One cost area traditionally analyzed and argued is that of processing the purchase order (PO) cycle for MRO. One process used to calculate the cost charts the PO paper flow through the requisitioner, to approval, to purchasing, to supplier quotes, to order placement, to receipt and to invoice payment. The total cost of personnel who perform these duties, divided by the number of POs placed per year is the processing cost of a single PO cycle. For example: U.S. Flan, a fictional company, creates ten thousand POs a year with yearly personnel costs of one million dollars. Therefore, the cost per PO is one hundred dollars. What?

E-procurement companies will propose programs that are designed to eliminate the cost of the PO cycle. They justify their implementation fees by stating, for example, that U.S. Flan will save one million dollars because the PO cycle is eliminated.

Good luck getting the CFO to sign off on it. Why? In the real world, MRO accounts for about ten percent of the company's total spend dollars, while generating about eighty percent of the transactions. This is a major reason why MRO becomes a target for e-procurement applications. Most CFOs will only agree to the savings projected if all the people who comprise the "personnel cost" go out the door. Again, in the real world, they do not leave. Why? In most cases, the personnel involved perform other duties than just PO processing. If the existing PO processing activities go away, the personnel are retained under Parkinson's Law: "Work expands to fill the time available to do it."

In addition, when e-procurement is installed, the MRO audit trail burden is shifted to other departments (just ask plant operations).

The particular study data in Figure 2.2 assumes the cost of processing a P. O. at fifty-seven dollars per. It also shows the imbalance of MRO spend versus burden generation. This study proports that by eliminating the PO/invoice cycle the company will save five hundred and seventy thousand dollars.

Again, good luck with your CFO!

**Figure 2.2:** Analysis: The imbalance of MRO spend dollars vs. total purchase order processing cost.

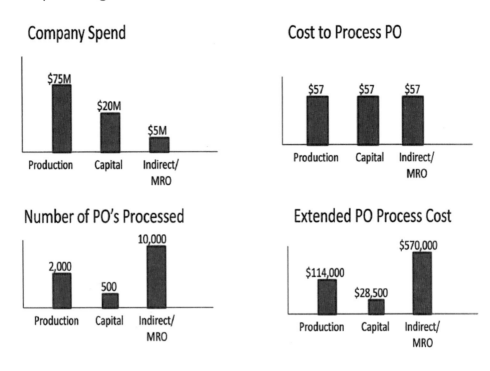

# THIRD-PARTY MRO, INTEGRATED SUPPLY, OUTSOURCING, INSOURCING, SYSTEMS CONTRACTING, VENDOR MANAGED INVENTORY AND A WHO KNOWS WHAT?

## INTEGRATED SUPPLY- WHAT'S IN A NAME?

*"If names are not correct, language will not be in accordance with the truth of things"*

– Confucius

When the supply concept of establishing the MRO distributor's function on-site within a manufacturer's facility becomes a reality, traditional distributors adopt a "Me, too!" position as a defensive measure. The process is known as integrated supply. Over the years, the term became mutated to describe any process that was different from the traditional requisition process (e.g., PO, delivery, invoice). Many failures have occurred under the integrated supply label to the detriment of the original concept.

If truth be told, traditional distributors would much prefer to remain traditional – "give me the order; it's my turn…let's go to lunch." What could be better for all concerned?

Many MRO consumers resist bringing a distributor on-site, stating, "We are astute in all that we do; we have huge purchasing power and can buy better than any distributor." The real world is that companies are astute within their core competency, but they are not so when it comes to managing a hardware store (i.e., the internal MRO storeroom).

These same companies have no problem hiring consultants, contractors, etc., to help them solve problems within their facilities. They contract with food service firms to operate their cafeterias. Companies do not buy eggs, bread, ham and cheese for their food service because they are not in the food business; they let the experts do it. So, why do companies continue to operate their own MRO storeroom when they are not in the storeroom business? Why don't they let the experts do it?

Maybe the resistance is all in the name. If the process referred to contractor services, would it receive a more positive consideration from plant management? Would contracted MRO operations (CMRO) be adopted rather than a cloudy defined integrated supply offering?

*What's in a name anyhow? …A rose is not always a rose under any other name.*

# INTEGRATED SUPPLY OR NOT? WHY OUTSOURCE MRO OPERATIONS?

Outsourcing of MRO to a third-party service provider is now emerging as a credible solution for organizations that would like to offer benefits beyond price reduction. Price savings alone can range from five to ten percent. Total ROI can reach twenty-five to thirty percent when measured on a TCO basis.

There are multiple flavors to outsourcing MRO, from piecemeal approaches involving sourcing through aggregators, vendor managed inventory (VMI) and procure to pay (P2P) outsourcing to end-to-end comprehensive outsourcing that spans across planning/forecasting, sourcing, procurement and inventory management. All these programs can be labeled integrated supply… the name game can be dangerous.

When an improvement process is labeled integrated supply and it fails, the failure will deny the company to try it again. Integrated supply should be defined as providing an optimum position for MRO's contribution to ROI and reliability.

A failed process labeled integrated supply that is a mutation of the proper process will deny further use of MRO's value potential.

> *"Why outsource MRO? With our purchasing power,*
> *we can do what our vendors do."*
> – CFO of a major food processer

When management states, "We should be able to do MRO ourselves," they show a lack of knowledge of the real world of the MRO supply chain. The industrial MRO consumer is not considered an authorized distributor by manufacturers who sell via distribution only…NO MATTER HOW HIGH THE SPEND.

Manufacturers provide resale discounts to their authorized distributors that are not available to industrial consumers (consumers are not distributors by definition). When companies go out on quote, they do not quote the manufacturer, they quote the distributor who has to squeeze down on the resale discount received from the manufacturer (the distributor's source of the product). There is only so much squeezing that can occur, even with site-specific special pricing, therefore, the RFQ process hits the wall and is only measured for a small number of SKUs (the infamous market basket). Distributors squeezed on the RFQ make up margin on spot, non-stock buys, which are not measured. The existing MRO process is replete with duplications and waste, thus containing significant cost reduction opportunities.

MRO consumers who operate their own storerooms exemplify duplications in the MRO supply chain, a cost that can be recovered by outsourcing.

Outsourcing has several meanings. It can mean sending work to China or other countries to be more competitive at the expense of American jobs. Outsourcing can also mean hiring companies to perform functions within their facilities that save American jobs. Outsourcing MRO to a third-party provider will reduce TCO and contribute to a company's bottom line. A company that is profitable is less likely to send jobs offshore.

# IMPLEMENTING MRO CHANGE

> *"It must be considered that there is nothing more difficult to carry out,*
> *nor more doubtful of success, nor more dangerous to handle,*
> *than to initiate a new order of things"*
> – Niccolo Machiavelli, "The Prince"

Machiavelli is saying that changing things is hard, might not be successful and unsafe to do, and that was in the 16th century.

Companies continually strive to improve their profit picture by investigating areas of cost that need/could be improved. Many areas of cost reduction opportunities exist in the industrial environment that purchasing managers are required to address as part of their job description goals.

Major opportunities are in the world of industrial MRO consumption and MRO storeroom management where huge values can be realized. However, these opportunities generally go untested, uninvestigated and underutilized.

Let's look at the cost recovery activity in the real world of MRO. First and foremost, the savings generated cannot be a detriment to plant reliability. The benefits of the cost recovery effort must accrue to all disciplines or the change will be defeated by someone.

As Mike Dyson, CIO of Storeroom Solutions, Inc., explains, "MRO is very transaction intensive. It accounts for a large chunk of overhead and the investment in MRO stores constitutes a profit drain rather than a profit-generating activity for any company who owns and operates its own MRO storeroom. The only way to reduce losses generated by MRO is to improve the effectiveness of the MRO supply chain. The cost to manage MRO parts from the source to the user in the plant is more important and more cost effective than a reduction in the piece price."

But here is the rub: How can we manage the MRO supply chain and still maintain and improve the duties necessary to optimize the financial opportunities available for the higher spend production related requirements? Could the answer be integrated supply? The question to this answer is, "What definition of the integrated supply process will achieve your financial and non-financial goals?" When you have that answer and are ready to implement the new program, you are ready for CHANGE! Remember what is written in "The Prince," CHANGE is difficult and dangerous.

The single, most important function necessary for a successful integrated supply program – without being difficult and dangerous – is to activate a proper implementation timeline and action list agreement.

According to Dyson, "If the selected supplier does not have a defined process and a history of successful implementations, including a director level staff assigned to implementation, it will fail. In addition, if any of the disciplines within the client's staff fail to support the implementation action items, the program will have ongoing problems and negative issues and it will ultimately fail."

If these factors are not in place, both parties are better off not instituting the change. History has proven this to be correct.

# ASSESSING VALUE

Companies will assess opportunities to identify which categories of cost are likely to have the greatest opportunity for financial improvement. This requires knowledge of:

- ➢ The existing market, supply preferences from plan disciplines, and the existing cost and process applied to each category under consideration;
- ➢ Internal factors constraining supply choices;
- ➢ Past sourcing efforts and expertise applied to managing the category.

When the category of MRO becomes a financial target for cost reduction, these are the considerations that need to be addressed:

- ➢ What are the financial goals to be obtained?
- ➢ How will change (improvement) affect each plant discipline?
- ➢ Is change possible in the current MRO situation?
- ➢ Are non-financial improvements recognized as part of the total financial improvement target?
- ➢ How are financial and non-financial improvements measured? How are they accepted as real contributions to the MRO financial recovery goals?

## EXAMPLES OF CHANGE GOALS

- ➢ Inventory turnover: From -1 to +6
- ➢ Inventory reduction: 35%
- ➢ Price Reduction: 5% in the aggregate
- ➢ Request to fill date: From 72% to 98.7%
- ➢ Spend reduction: 30%
- ➢ Freight reduction: 4.5%
- ➢ Warranty recovery: 90%
- ➢ Obsolescence recovery: 75%

➢ Supplier consolidation: From 288 to 6

➢ Transaction reduction: From 18,000 to 24

*THE STOREROOM'S TOTAL COST OF OWNERSHIP*
*IS NOW AT OPTIMUM*

## INSTITUTING NEW STANDARD OPERATING PROCEDURES FOR MRO OPERATIONS.

Create a personalized scope of work with the selected provider; include the following actions:

➢ **Identification:** SKUs versus material equipment list (MEL)

➢ **Planning:** Bill of materials (BOMs), failure modes and effects analysis (FMEA)

➢ **Scheduling:** Backlog management, mean time to repair (MTTR)

➢ **Execution:** Kitting, staging

➢ **Implementing:** Most important factor; do it correctly or not at all

➢ **Reporting:** Failure mode and effects analysis (FMEA)

➢ **Maintaining:** Communicating CMMS data

*THE STOREROOM IS NOW CONNECTED TO*
*LEAN MAINTENANCE INCENTIVES*

**Figure 3.1:** Complete an ROI analysis

\*  Includes both financial and non-financial cost
\*\*  Includes values acquired with revised SOP coordinated with maintenance reliability

## *TIME TO CHANGE?*
### Ask Yourself : In House or Third Party?

Write New SOP for MRO                    Outsource MRO

**In-House required**

**Third-Party required**

The Seven "As"

- Acknowledge
- Acquire Knowledge
- Assign
- Approve Financing
- Accept Provider
- Administrative
- Adjust

*Can you accomplish these functions required for success?*

The Eight "Cs"

- Capable
- Core Competency
- Commercial Success
- Commitment
- Calamity Avoidance
- Camaraderie
- Capitalized Value
- Change Experts

*Will this turnkey solution be accepted by plant disciplines?*

# INSIGHTFUL QUESTIONS INTO THE MRO WORLD

In a recent roundtable session centered on the world of the MRO supply chain, there were many questions put forth for discussion. Here are the five most active questions and this author's opinionated answers.

1. **How is integrated supply different from traditional, horizontal supply chain activity? What are the advantages and disadvantages of integrated supply?**

   To answer this question with any degree of accuracy, there are questions that must be answered first.

> ➤ What is the reader's definition of integrated supply?
> ➤ What position does the reader hold in the MRO supply chain?
> ➤ Where did the reader obtain information about integrated supply – hands-on experience? Someone's literature? RFQ?

As the integrated supply concept transformed the industrial supply industry, multiple definitions and processes were labeled integrated supply based on who was talking, where they were in the supply chain and their profit goals. There is one traditional distribution company who has a listing of nine…count 'em… nine separate program offerings it calls integrated supply. The obvious problem is if a company with an MRO problem chooses one of these nine programs and it does not solve that company's MRO problems, the label integrated supply would be forever forbidden as a solution. Even worse, if the program fails because of the supplier's lack of commitment, experience, etc., the company would never try "that thing again," thereby denying the company all the value that can be released from a world-class third-party MRO storeroom operation, no matter what you call it.

For purposes of this answer, let's define integrated supply as a process that places a single source MRO supplier on-site within the client's facilities who manages all the functions necessary for that client to realize ALL the values available from a personalized world-class MRO operation.

The difference between a traditional, horizontal supply chain and integrated supply can be simply described as:

> ➤ TRADITIONAL MRO SUPPLY CHAIN: The client determines that certain quantities of SKUs need to be replaced in stock in the storeroom; a purchase order is generated to fulfill the need (paperwork). The traditional supplier receives an order from the client in various ways (e.g., mail, phone, electronically, etc.), the order is processed internally (paperwork) and shipped to the client's receiving dock (paperwork). The client receives the shipment (paperwork) and moves the shipment to the MRO storeroom or directly to the requisitioner. The supplier sends an invoice to the client for material shipped (paperwork) and the client matches the invoice to what was received and authorizes payment (paperwork). The supplier receives payment and satisfies the shipment audit trail.

➢ INTEGRATED SUPPLY CHAIN: The on-site supplier who manages the MRO store issues the requested part to an authorized requisitioner and the shipment is complete. A twice per month invoice is generated for parts issued or placed in stock with all audit controls required by the client. Most parts are consumed before the invoice is presented.

There are numerous advantages of integrated supply based on how the client chooses to apply the activities. These are the most prevalent:

➢ The client can concentrate on its core area of expertise and be relieved of MRO problems.

➢ Stores become a part of the maintenance mantra and act in support of maintenance programs.

➢ Stores now have a responsibility to contribute to plant and product reliability.

➢ The client's TCO is drastically reduced.

➢ The on-site supplier is held to performance standards via measured KPIs developed in concert with the client's needs.

Perceived disadvantages of integrated supply are largely subjective in nature and come under these headings:

➢ "We are a large corporation and can buy better than suppliers and save their fees."

➢ "We go out on quote when a contract is terminated because it is written in our SOP."

➢ "We do not want all our eggs in one basket; we need to continually test the market."

The major disadvantage of integrated supply is the failure of a selected supplier to recognize the commitment necessary to be successful. A failed program labeled integrated supply will not be tried again and all the potential benefits are lost.

There are no objective disadvantages to a clearly defined integrated supply program that retains a qualified provider who maintains its commitments to the KPIs and continual improvements year after year. A company hires security companies and outsources the cafeteria because it is not in those businesses. The same thinking should be applied to MRO; the company is not in the hardware store business.

2. **How can a business determine if MRO inventory sharing is right for it?**

As in Question #1, what is the definition of inventory sharing? If it means sharing inventory among company-owned plants, it can be effective IF there is proper administration. Plant A may have an excess of a #1234 gear motor and be willing to send one to Plant B who has an emergency, unless Plant A is unwilling to share for fear of a shutdown. If a number of plants have stock of a particular SKU and usage is "just in case," there could be an agreement to have just one site keep an agreed quantity and the other plants reduce inventory accordingly.

If inventory sharing is defined as stock on hold at the supplier, there must be a firm agreement as to whom is responsible for the inventory should the plant decrease or eliminate usage.

In either case, inventory sharing is viable and has benefits if it is administered by a third-party MRO provider (integrated supplier?). The key is to share inventory and not have an out of stock situation that causes downtime.

Businesses can determine if sharing is right for them if they experience inventory reductions without emergencies and downtime; there must be sustained management of the process.

3. **Can you explain the benefits of MRO inventory reduction and the management challenges associated with the process?**

MRO inventory represents one of the major factors that contribute to unprofitable and unreliable MRO stores' operations. Plant disciplines are in conflict over inventories, with maintenance wanting more, finance wanting less, purchasing buying less for a lower price and engineering changing processes that cause obsolescence and added SKUs.

In addition, if MRO inventory is listed as an asset rather than an expense when purchased, management is reluctant to write off obsolete stock because of the impact on the balance sheet and the profit and loss (P&L) statement.

Reduced inventory has the advantage of reducing financial expenses and freeing dollars for other opportunities. Management has the challenge of reducing MRO inventory to contribute to plant profitability while making sure parts are on hand when needed and in the quantity needed – a daunting task when store decisions are made by personnel with conflicting goals.

A 3PMRO provider would be required to own and manage its owned stock on-site and invoice the client after the inventory is issued and consumed. This provider also would be required to maintain an agreed fill rate to ensure no downtime. The plant now experiences instant and continuing inventory recovery while contributing to plant reliability goals.

It is relatively easy to reduce MRO inventory, either cut min-max quantities or just stop replacement orders. In the real MRO world, should this happen, there is the conceived danger of shutdowns, so maintenance engineers will "buy around" the storeroom, resulting in increased and uncontrolled substocks. Inventory reductions must be coordinated with inventory rightsizing to be safe and effective.

**4.  How can the industry start to change from the mind-set that improvement projects are expenditures, not investments?**

First, let's look at the real world of MRO operations. In general, companies view MRO as a necessary evil that cannot be improved and, if it were, who would do it, what is to be done and who will pay for it? MRO is but six to ten percent of the total spend, so most companies will spend time on the ninety percent of what they purchase. But as it stands, MRO represents the largest percentage of cost improvement opportunity available. Experience shows that for the same effort, MRO yielded twenty-five to thirty percent compared to two to three percent for production materials.

Companies invest considerable dollars in maintenance reliability programs to increase asset reliability and provide a reliable plant. The effects of these programs are depleted when the storerooms remain unreliable. When maintenance is in a failure mode and the required part is not available, maintenance fails and the asset is not reliable, which makes for an unreliable product.

If industry would recognize that MRO stores are an essential part of the reliability process, it would also recognize that MRO change is an investment and not an expense, as long as it is implemented and sustained properly.

**5.  What is the perfect storeroom?**

A perfect storeroom is one that satisfies all the needs of all plant disciplines all the time. Maintenance engineers have all the parts in the quantities needed, when needed and they have eliminated their backup substocks as a guard against stock outs because there are never any stock outs. Stores management is totally connected to the investment the plant has made in reliability programs and finance and purchasing are happy with the prices paid and do not require inventory reduction or limitations. Most of all, the plant manager spends no time on MRO complaints because the storeroom is perfect by definition. In the real MRO world, there is no such thing as a "perfect" storeroom and none to be had. To be in an optimum cost position, a company should not be in the storeroom business in the first place.

# WHY CAN'T WE DO IT OURSELVES?

There are times when companies recognize that change in the operation of MRO stores is necessary to achieve support of reliable assets, hence, a reliable product.

Attempts to achieve an MRO solution that will provide optimum benefits often fall short of stated goals and way short of the potential benefits that can be achieved. Many companies believe that they are most proficient in all things relating to management excellence and, as a result, will apply their skills to the world of MRO. Here are objective reasons why companies cannot achieve optimum MRO in spite of their high level of intelligence in areas of their expertise.

1. The industrial MRO consumer is not positioned in the MRO supply chain to realize functional discounts or eliminate supply chain activities that limit purchasing power.

   ➤ Manufacturers who sell products via distributors will not, except in rare occasions, sell around their distributors to the MRO consumers. In a food industry study, a major food company tried to negotiate purchase prices from manufacturers. But the food company was not able to negotiate MRO purchase prices from manufacturers at reduced or discounted levels the way third-party MRO providers are able to do.

   ➤ Selling directly (manufacturer to user) does not eliminate the existing cost of distribution. Either the user or the manufacturer shoulders the distribution costs; the costs do not go away. In the major food company case study, it did not have the personnel, systems, or controls in its supply chain to eliminate distribution costs, nor was it able to invest in the personnel to do so.

➢ Manufacturers in many industries have distributors because it is not economical for them to process orders and ship to all potential MRO users, let alone exercise sales and marketing programs. Manufacturers will franchise their distributors and will not sell directly to clients of those distributors, regardless of spend volume.

2. The industrial MRO consumer routinely creates a significant number of transactions through an extensive supplier base that cannot be significantly reduced internally.

➢ The nature of MRO orders carries a wide diversity of products spread out over many categories and many suppliers. The average MRO order is five hundred dollars. The number of transactions for any manufacturer would increase prohibitively, as would the transactions for the user, if all MRO supplies were to be purchased directly.

➢ The MRO storeroom in the major food company study had annual purchases of over twenty-five million dollars based on over seventy-five thousand transactions using approximately two hundred and sixty-five active suppliers, who were quite fragmented to manage.

➢ More than one hundred other site studies involving manufacturers and MRO consumers in the food, pharmaceutical, newspaper, automotive, material handling, and pulp and paper industries, identified that eight percent of MRO dollars creates eighty percent of user transactions. This contributed to a significant administrative and personnel hidden cost.

3. The concept of bringing the provider on-site so the user is out of the internal distribution business is designed to reduce total cost of ownership for the industrial/institutional MRO consumer.

➢ Optimum cost reduction comes from eliminating an existing step in the MRO supply chain. If MRO consumers do it themselves, there is no step elimination and optimum cost reductions are not realized. The major food company realized this fact when conducting its MRO outsourcing evaluation.

➢ If an on-site supplier can demonstrate it has no traditional distribution burden in its financial proposal, there will be a step eliminated and the resulting cost savings will be realized by the MRO consumer.

➢ By placing the MRO distribution function on-site and requiring the MRO provider to treat the on-site store as a branch of its operations, a true cost step is removed from the process with optimum benefit for the MRO consumer. In the major food company case study, this change produced a net savings of over four million dollars.

➢ Traditional distributors who also attempt to be MRO integrators maintain warehouses, local stocks and all costs associated with MRO distribution. When the traditional integrator obtains an on-site integrated client, there is some related cost reduction for the MRO consumer, however, there is no elimination of a cost step in the supply chain. The traditional distributer's integrated supply program will eventually fail because it cannot deliver year after year savings.

In the continual search for cost recovery, the MRO consumer will seek the ultimate solution – to be out of the stores business completely. This solution only can be attained from a pure integrator, one who has no traditional MRO revenue.

➢ Traditional distributors who operate/incorporate their so-called integrated supply programs have done so from a defensive position. Traditional distributors make more profit with traditional purchase orders than they do with integrated supply scenarios. This is the reason many integrators are retreating from the concept.

➢ A distributor's profitability considerations dictate that the integrated function must utilize the inventories of the corporation and assume a proportionate share of corporate overhead. These considerations are apparent in the financial proposals to the industrial MRO consumer. The effect is an improvement, but the optimum cost position is not achieved for the MRO consumer.

4.  By definition, MRO consumers will continue to own inventory if they do it themselves. If they utilize vendor stocking, there would be multiple suppliers to manage and audit, creating higher administrative costs and adding more internal employees.

    ➢ The unpredictable nature of MRO usage causes stock units to vacillate between repetitive and just in case usage. For the supplier, inventory control and the burden of all SKUs would be unacceptable. Due to the unpredictable nature of MRO usage in the case study, the food company experienced a poor seventy-six percent fill rate, which contributed to a downtime total of two hundred and eighty-nine hours, another hidden cost.

    ➢ Generally, onetime, non-stock buys constitute twenty-five to thirty percent of the MRO dollar expenditure. If an MRO consumer elects to do it itself, the burden of the onetimers remains with the MRO consumer, with little control of prices and little recognition of repetitiveness.

    ➢ If service levels from the MRO storeroom remain inadequate, onetime spot buys increase, which, in turn, increases inventory (dollars) in substocks, thus creating more unprofitable risk for the company.

5.  In many companies where MRO considerations are in the hands of maintenance, MRO stores' personnel will focus on managing transactions and do little sourcing because there is little time available due to too many stock outs, rushes, etc. The function of searching, sourcing and frequently pricing is accomplished by the MRO consumer's planners and requisitioners, taking time from more productive duties.

# CONSIDER COMPANIES THAT HAVE DECIDED TO DO IT THEMSELVES

They exist in two categories:

1. Those that have tried third parties and/or integrated supply and <u>failed</u>.
2. Those that have a strong corporate indirect materials (MRO) purchasing department and have invested heavily in SAP-type computer systems and long term price agreements designed to place MRO orders electronically.

In the first category, the MRO consumer has been burned and is reluctant to try again. This is a result of integrators who think coming on-site is a simple task and do not understand the commitment necessary for success. Many so-called integrators do not understand the additional costs they incur until they realize that returns are inadequate when they enter into agreements without the necessary management controls. Opportunity costs become excessive; the failed distributor realizes that there is more profit in the traditional market and does not take the necessary steps to be successful in a third party MRO operation.

In the second category, it is us (corporate purchasing) versus them (the plant), or vice versa. Corporate price agreements are reached with national suppliers who exist as a result of the flawed market basket procedure. Pricing from suppliers is based on estimated (mostly overestimated) dollar consumption for the corporation. Plant personnel invariably can beat the corporate price on any given day to the detriment of the corporate agreement. Compliance is always a question, the level of which is directly proportionate to the strength of corporate purchasing. If a given site within a corporation recognizes the financial and non-financial benefits of hiring an expert third-party MRO supplier to operate its MRO stores, it is perceived by some in corporate purchasing as a threat to their department and a sapping of usage volume from the commitment to the selected national MRO suppliers. At times, corporate purchasing fights the third-party outsourcing program stating that, if one plant goes with on-site supply and does not/cannot use the corporate MRO suppliers, the prices will go up for the other non-participating sites.

Nothing could be further from the truth. The corporate MRO suppliers will recognize competition and either offer the third-party MRO a discount or reduce its corporate MRO prices. At the very least, they will not raise prices; what purchasing person would let them? Remember, corporate purchasing and the supply base cannot get compliance if the local plants decide to use its preferred supply base. If forced, the locals can slow down, show lower production, prove out of stock situations *and* beat the corporate purchasing price.

Who gains? Who profits? The success of a 3PMRO program requires the cooperation of all disciplines and the recognition that benefits accrue to all.

# IMPLEMENTING LEAN INITIATIVES; ELIMINATING WASTE (MUDA)

By implementing lean initiatives, companies can knock down supply chain barriers, thus optimizing total cost of ownership. Key lean initiatives encompass:

- ➤ Outsourcing to a third-party MRO provider to manage the purchasing and inventory of MRO items across all company locations. This eliminates or reduces the waste of traditional distributors, commissioned sales, purchasing transactions and accounting transactions.
- ➤ Third-party MRO provider personnel residing within company locations, improving the productivity of company personnel (e.g., planners, maintenance, purchasing, receiving, finance, and human resources).
- ➤ Performance requirements established to ensure:
  - ○ High service levels;
  - ○ Management visibility and control;
  - ○ Inventory control;
  - ○ Cost reductions related to unit prices, transaction costs, freight ○ costs and warranty recovery;
  - ○ Productivity improvements related to downtime, fill rates, people and capital.
- ➤ Third-party MRO provider guaranteeing financial and non-financial goals measured by mutual KPI agreement.

When companies invest dollars in lean initiatives for plant operations, measurable benefits accrue. When dollars are not invested in MRO to achieve similar lean objectives, the return of investment factor is lacking.

When lean efforts and MRO outsourcing principles are implemented collectively, the company's bottom line will amass a measurable ROI value at an optimum level.

# RESISTANCE TO CHANGE – TOP FIVE SCENARIOS

Even when the consensus in a plant recognizes that MRO operations are inadequate and considered trivial, there are always some associates who will put forth reasons to keep the status quo.

In addition to some people's basic resistance to change *anything*, the "this is the way we have always done it" or "if it ain't broke, don't fix it" thinkers, here are five situations that can deter the need to change.

1. THE INCUMBENT IS FACED WITH MRO ON-SITE COMPETITION

   The company is familiar with the local supplier and the local supplier has done a creditable job with respect to showing up, handling emergencies, etc. The incumbent, in most cases, doesn't have the ability or has not been able to recognize the value of offering total cost reduction. If the incumbent has not been proactive in offering price and/or cost savings, the company should question the incumbent's ability and desire to bring true cost reduction to the customer when faced with competition. Why is the incumbent suddenly able to help the customer reduce costs from the same off-site distribution situation when faced with the loss of business? How can the incumbent maintain off-site costs, come on-site (with costs) and still provide an optimum cost position for the client? The answer is they cannot; the additional costs are paid by the client.

2. DECISION MADE TO PURCHASE BY PRODUCT CATEGORY

   This is the safer way for a company to go; it provides job protection for the decision maker, committees remain intact and there is no out on a limb situation. This is, at best, a minimum interim cost reduction situation; further cost reductions will be required to reach the optimum cost position. In addition, solutions that are not at optimum create substantial opportunity costs that are lost and never recovered. The myriad so-called integrated supply programs rarely provide total cost of ownership benefits because all available cost recovery opportunities are not realized.

3. "GOOD OL' BOY" NETWORK

   This is different than incumbency because the good ol' boy network provides far more than product, service, price, etc. Costs are increased because the perks offered must be covered in margins. Decision makers may not want to give up the perks.

4.  TECHNOLOGY

    The aura of e-procurement becomes a desirable path to take in the modern age of technology. The projected cost savings and efficiencies are dramatic. However, this is not the case for MRO. Lumping MRO expenditures into the total electronic consideration can help justify the cost of installing e-procurement methods for all purchased categories. This is at the cost of a reliable storeroom because e-procurement methods do not address all the financial and non-financial needs of world-class MRO functions.

5.  LOCAL STOCK ADVANTAGE

    Detractors will point to the advantages they have enjoyed by having local suppliers respond to their emergency needs. A world class storeroom operated on-site by a committed provider would minimize emergencies by coordinating with maintenance (a part of proper scope of work). The expert provider has the critical spares (emergencies) on the shelf on site in the quantities needed and/or has remedies ready for extraordinary situations.

# THE MRO MINEFIELD: 50 WAYS TO LOSE YOUR PROGRAM

*The purchase of a home is the most important investment people make. With over 10,000 settlements occurring each day in the USA, one would think that the process should be routine without flaws. Not so! I have experienced a long list of incidents that cause delays and cancellations, and the list is still growing. To minimize these barriers is to anticipate, prepare and be ready for the unknown.*

–Kenneth B. Krauter, Realtor

Managing MRO to the satisfaction of ALL personnel is a minefield. Before entering this mine-field called MRO, you should be aware of the location of those mines so you can disarm them. Managing the MRO store may seem a simple task, after all, how difficult can it be, it's just a STORE, right? Wrong!

Any change program will have its detractors. Even programs that have true value and direction from senior management to implement will have people from all levels who will think of ways to defeat the process. From real-life experiences, here are the top 50 ways – and five more for good measure – to defeat an on-site MRO cost reduction program. The consequences are indicated in brackets.

1. Add functions to the scope of work without allowing labor increase. [This defeats value, mitigates efficiency.]
2. Allow purchasing cards (p-cards) to authorize purchases around the program. [You will lose price leverage and increase opportunity costs.]
3. Approve new brand then claim unauthorized substitutions. [This disrupts operations.]
4. Buy and create substocks. [You will lose price leverage, increase inventory and defeat value.]
5. Buy inventory parts as a onetime. [This will create obsolete inventory and increase inventory.]
6. Change the value of the buy. [This disrupts ROI analysis.]
7. Create spot buy emergencies for single source parts. [You claim lack of response, causing downtime.]
8. Draw out large quantities and put into substocks. [This causes stock outs.]
9. Draw out max quantity and then enter a request for the same SKU. [This creates stock outs and causes downtime.]
10. False generalization Part #1 – Do not recognize cost of money benefits in the ROI. [The entire ROI is false.]
11. False generalization Part #2 – "All of our prices include freight so we have no freight costs." [Freight is a fact of life; it is in there somewhere.]
12. False generalization Part #3 – "We receive no benefit of transaction reduction we have the people anyway, so there are no savings." [Requires personnel management for value to occur…can take on new duties without new hires]
13. False generalization Part #4 – "Inventory reduction is not a benefit, corporate does not charge us with the cost of money." [Why not buy 100 of everything? Now see what corporate has to say.]
14. False generalization Part #5 – Share provider's financials with supplier "buddies" to prove lack of value. [Some short run benefit to budget holder…creates long run cost increases]
15. False generalization Part #6 – "You cannot buy as well as we do. We have buyers." [This reasoning does not recognize the company's position in the supply chain; company cannot buy MRO where the provider buys.]

16. False generalization Part #7 – "You never have anything." [In reality, fill rates are at ninety-nine percent per KPI agreement; just one complaint about a single incident can balloon rates.]

17. Indigenous descriptions utilized. [This causes inventory duplications and increases SKUs.]

18. Insignificant and erroneous data regarding last price paid, unit of measure and descriptions. [Causes aura of lack of price performance; constitutes inaccurate measurement.]

19. Lack of information on critical spares. [Deliberate miscommunication to cause downtime.]

20. Maintain acrimonious attitude toward provider's on-site personnel. [Causes turnover, lack of performance, and a bad work environment.]

21. Place order for SKU that exists in provider's owned inventory. [Claim the provider has charged for existing company-owned inventory.]

22. Price – call the provider's source, get its price. [Claim price is high.]

23. Price – compare current price to old last price paid. [Claim high price.]

24. Price – compare low quality parts price to designated quality brands. [Claim price is high.]

25. Price – get a local supplier to lowball a couple of requisitions. [Claim high price.]

26. Price – request spot buy for quantity of one, compare price to quantity of five. [Claim high price.]

27. Price – require single source, get source to increase price to provider. [Claim price is high.]

28. Proclaim: "It will not work." [Maintain self-fulfilling prophecy, find fault with all actions and offer no help.]

29. Protect one's empire. [Places individual goals above corporate progress. It also fosters resistance and offers no help.]

30. Provide inadequate descriptions and install wrong parts. [Causes increased downtime and production delays.]

31. Recommend improper min/max quantities. [Causes stock outs and increases inventory.]

32. Refuse brand change benefits. [Defeats productivity.]

33. Refuse to recognize that inventory reduction reduces cost of money expenditure. [Dilutes ROI.]

34. Refuse to recognize transaction elimination as a savings. [Does not recognize the value of time recovery.]

35. Refuse to use approved brands. [Defeats value; increases price paid]]
36. Relocate stock during off-hours without authorization or notification. [Causes stock outs, duplicated inventory.]
37. Remove categories from the program. [Decreases value opportunity.]
38. Remove functions from the program. [Devalues the process.]
39. Remove new SKUs without authorization and replace them with used parts. [Brings accusations of misconduct.]
40. Remove parts on dark hours and request the parts during store hours. [Creates downtime.]
41. Request new part, return it with components missing. [Causes faulty situation when reissued.]
42. Require existing clerks to be hired by provider without controls. [Creates multiple opportunities to defeat the process.]
43. Require multiple stock locations by machine type. [Duplicates SKUs and increases inventory.]
44. Require unnecessary IT, financial functions and reporting, creating a profit drain for the provider. [Adds costs for user, creates a lack of trust and causes opportunity costs.]
45. Require use of a local, longtime supplier. [Eliminates value of purchasing power.]
46. Require use of long-term agreements (LTAs). [Eliminates the value of the provider's purchasing power.]
47. Provide no positive support to help the provider meet guarantees and shared savings goals. [Causes provider to write checks, lose money and trigger possible termination.]
48. Set up new SKU numbers for existing parts. [Increases inventory and obsolescence.]
49. Skew testing on new parts. [Defeats productivity opportunities.]
50. Target provider's fee for reductions. [ Reductions in the provider's fee can cause program failure and loss of opportunity for the company.]

*Here are five more for good measure:*
1. Claim all SKUs are critical spares, including miscellaneous consumable items "rope, soap and dope". [Allows any stock out to be blamed for downtime.]
2. Discredit the audit trail after the fact by claiming infringement of the Sarbanes-Oxley Act (SOX). [Obfuscates the facts, installs fear of auditors.]

3. Maintain fear of the unknown: "I will not sign up because I will have egg on my face if it fails." [Protects status quo to be safe at the cost of releasing existing value.]

4. "New broom sweeps clean" – New executive brings own philosophy and reverts to traditional distribution, claiming to save the provider's fee, buy where providers buy. [Achieves short-term price success, and covers up long-term assumption of stores' total cost of operations. Rarely admits mistakes.]

5. Create a pseudo purchase order with a price much lower than the provider's price; use the PO to prove that the provider has high pricing. Never place the purchase order. [False actions bordering on libel. Adds the cost necessary to defend false accusations.]

# MRO CASE STUDIES

## U.S. FLAN: THE BEST DANG FLAN IN THE WORLD

U.S. Flan is a fictitious company with real MRO problems: U.S. Flan is in the hardware store business and does not know it.

Traditional distributors buy miscellaneous MRO consumables, put them into inventory and sell them at a profit to their client, U.S. Flan, which also puts them into inventory. The distributors pay for heat, light, brick and mortar and clerks, and make a profit. The profit made is a function of how many times a dollar of inventory can be turned over. For example, when the Flan supplier buys a bolt for a dollar and sells it for a dollar fifty, if it turns six times, it amounts to three dollars (six times fifty cents markup and is profitable for the supplier. The investment in inventory is profitable because of the turnover ratio.

Compare this to U.S. Flan, which assumes the "necessary" cost of an MRO storeroom (must-have parts on hand to support flan production). Flan's purchasing buys six bolts for one dollar and fifty cents, all of which goes into MRO stores. The stores issue and charge the users or asset one dollar and fifty cents (note there is no markup). MRO inventory does not turn more than once in the most efficient MRO operations; at U.S. Flan, the turn is negative one. They buy six bolts for stock, but only use five a year and make no markup when they issue [sell?] parts to their workers; therefore, they are in a loosing money situation right from the start.

The total spend for MRO is seven percent of the total purchasing budget for all products, including the ingredients for flan. However, the number of transactions created for MRO is sixty-five percent of all transactions created. So, U.S. Flan as a distributor of MRO, albeit internal, makes zero markup, has a negative inventory turn with a twenty percent out of stock performance and upside down paper processing costs. If U.S. Flan can do it themselves, i.e. change to a world-class MRO operation, why does the condition continue to exist? The truth is that U.S. Flan's position in the supply chain will not allow it to eliminate the duplicated steps that exist in the same supply chain.

While trying to be the best darn flan company in the world, U.S. Flan is being dragged down by the cost drain of MRO stores. What to do? Consider this question: *"Why is U.S. Flan in the MRO business? All it wants to do is make and sell flan!" It is not a home improvement specialty retailer, so it should not be in the hardware store business.*

# WHOSE PROGRAM IS IT ANYWAY?

The president and CEO of fictitious U.S. Flan called T.M. Doyle (fictitiously real) in corporate procurement and told him seventy million dollars needed to be taken out of his spend over the next three years.

Well now, thought Doyle, it's not going to come from ingredients because sales are up and more ingredients need to be purchased to produce more flan. The chickens will lay only as many eggs as they want; the company could buy more chickens, but more space will be needed and that increases spend. What to do? U.S. Flan could go lean, consolidate manufacturing footprints, gain more productivity from personnel, institute more effective processing actions and … wait a minute … what about those indirect spend dollars? The company does not spend any purchasing time on MRO because it is only seven percent of its spend, therefore, suppliers charge whatever they want and the company accepts it as a cost of doing business, sort of like electricity.

Doyle finally saw MRO for what it really was – a cost that is not recovered in the manufacturing process. Some investigating revealed that a ten percent recovery would put Doyle fifteen percent into his goal. A twenty percent recovery would be thirty percent and leave only seventy percent to be gained elsewhere. Who would have thought MRO contained that much value opportunity? Doyle found that MRO created eighty percent of the paperwork, accounted for seventy-two percent of the number of suppliers and was the easiest and quickest path to his recovery requirements. It was settled, he was going to get out of the storeroom business!

With painful investigation into the maze of MRO programs that distributors call integrated supply, Doyle was able to isolate one that had the ability to completely release him from the burden of MRO stores.

## HOW TO SELL THIS INTERNALLY?

MRO users in each plant had their entrenched suppliers and they defended them at every turn with comments like: "We must buy locally to support our community. "Old Ben has been in here for fifteen years and has saved us on weekends many times over; he was in here on Easter Sunday one year." And the biggie: "You purchasing guys are not going to tell us how to run our plant."

So, Doyle's program was installed and implemented in a pilot plant. Nothing went right; maintenance found everything wrong.

- "Parts are different." (Approved subs were later dubbed "substitutions"with a sneer.)
- "They never have anything." (Supplier reports showed ninety-eight percent full rates, up from seventy-two percent, so they must have something.)
- "They caused downtime." (The second shift took parts and did not record them, causing deliberate stock outs.)
- "Prices are higher." (Maintenance claimed, "I could have bought that file cheaper from old Ben.")
- "We need technical support on all parts." (Would that be soap/dope/rope also?)

The program began to fall apart because of resistance, lack of proactive communications, and out-and-out sabotage.

Why? It was not facilities' program; it was not invented there.

Doyle went to the VP of operations who, it was revealed, was also asked to cut eight million dollars a month from his budget. The two went at it over who should get credit for the value of the MRO change. They did not argue that there was value, just who would get the credit when it was made to work properly. They agreed to share the benefits that would accrue if cooperation was established.

Reporting modifications were made, plants were added and the program was renamed. It was now the "President's Spend Saving Technology" program or PSST, which got everyone's attention and cooperation. The president simply said that anyone who finds objections must put forth ideas that will overcome the objections. In other words, "How would you do it better?" The fact that maintenance reported to the VP of operations certainly aided cooperation and eliminated disruptions.

Goals were exceeded and all involved were relieved of the MRO burden. They were now free to pursue other more important spend reduction pursuits.

Lesson learned: Your program can fail if you fail to obtain buy-in from all affected by the change. Your program can fail if you fail to show benefits to all plant disciplines. You also need the support of the boss.

# THE CONSULTANT'S VS. THE 3PMRO ON-SITE PROVIDER'S VIEW

## STATE OF MRO AT U.S. FLAN

- ➤ Substantial spend spread across multiple sites and categories; not defined/measured
- ➤ Many unique SKUs, many of which are used only on certain equipment; duplications
- ➤ Unpredictable demand – some seventy percent of MRO items turn less than once every two years
- ➤ A "just in case" mind frame, buying more than actually needed; substocks abound
- ➤ Large number of vendors, including local vendors, at individual sites
- ➤ Spot buys – unplanned purchases can account for fifty percent of total MRO spend
- ➤ Data management challenges – myriad number of specs, part numbering, systems and more
- ➤ Recommendations of best practices are not sustained and/or not fully implemented
- ➤ Strong attachments to existing suppliers
- ➤ Stronger management focus on the need to change the MRO process

T.M. Doyle, the CPO at U.S. Flan, entertained two proposals designed to solve his MRO problems.

| THE CONSULTANT'S PROPOSAL | THE 3PMRO ON-SITE PROVIDER'S PROPOSAL |
|---|---|
| **MRO Strategy: Client Performs**<br>• The MRO procurement strategy is focused on creating strategic advantages<br>• Regional and category specific issues/constraints are understood and addressed<br>• Category strategies are developed and communicated across the enterprise | **MRO Strategy: On-Site Provider Performs**<br>• Focused on supplier's best cost; 3PMRO purchasing power<br>• OEM commercialization<br>• New product administration<br>• 3PMRO central purchasing strategies applied<br>• Effectiveness measured via agreed KPIs |
| **Organizational Alignment:**<br>• MRO procurement is not perceived as a high value generator by top management<br>• Center-led procurement drives the development of global MRO procurement strategies, policies and processes executed at the local level and assigns category management responsibility for key categories to company personnel | **Organizational Alignment:**<br>• MRO generally considered low value, low priority opportunity<br>• MRO operations connected to lean/reliability maintenance programs at each site via personalized SOPs<br>• Discipline conflicts resolved<br>• On-site provider performs functions |
| **Sourcing:**<br>• All categories are sourced and revisited by cross functional teams<br>• Enterprise spend is leveraged<br>• Procurement is a key driver behind simplification and standardization of sourced products and services<br>• Sourcing focuses on strategic suppliers, thus reducing the size of the supply base | **Sourcing:**<br>• Total 3PMRO spend is leveraged, not just the client spend<br>• Duplications are minimized<br>• Substitutions approved with SOS control<br>• Cross functional teams are generally dysfunctional on sourcing issues<br>• Supply base reduced to one |

*Continued on next page*

*Continued*

| THE CONSULTANT'S PROPOSAL | THE 3PMRO ON-SITE PROVIDER'S PROPOSAL |
|---|---|
| **Procurement Technology :**<br>• Proactively uses technology to manage the MRO program<br>• Heavy usage of strategic sourcing tools, such as eRFX, auctions, contract management<br>• Heavy use of spend management tools to understand and manage MRO expenditures and compliance<br>• Highly automated procurement processes<br>• Focused on online ordering, invoicing and payment per shipment | **Procurement Technology:**<br>• Provider is connected to and complies with existing client's IT requirements<br>• Client's LTAs are utilized<br>• Stores' inventory connected to lean/reliable maintenance initiatives<br>• Client purchase order cycles are eliminated<br>• Invoices twice monthly for parts issued |
| **Inventory Management:**<br>• Segment items by asset criticality<br>• Proactively monitor usage to balance asset availability and inventory cost<br>• Adjust usage forecasts at a minimum annually<br>• Selective use of VMI/consignment to drive down inventory costs<br>• Utilize SLAs to define expectations and KPIs to monitor effectiveness | **Inventory Management:**<br>• Inventory management connected to maintenance reliability requirements<br>• Obsolescence recovered substocks minimized<br>• 3PMRO-owned inventory on-site in stores; payment after use |
| **Procurement Process:**<br>• Transaction-oriented procurement activities are actively being eliminated<br>• Orders are transmitted electronically<br>• U.S. Flan still has purchase orders to place<br>• U.S. Flan still receives parts for stock | **Procurement Process:**<br>• On-site stores' operations are the core of 3PMRO's revenues<br>• There are no purchase orders for U.S. Flan to place nor parts to receive and stock<br>• 3PMRO physically manages entire MRO process, it's not just a recommendation; this effects measured sustainability and KPI improvements |

The MRO spend and MRO inventory values are not defined (unknown). At U.S. Flan, MRO spend values vary by one hundred to two hundred percent according to which discipline is answering the question. Storeroom data is questionable and does not include all spend and inventory. The real world is that the MRO expenditure is not known and the dollar value of inventory is not accurate.

The consultant states that: "KPIs are utilized to monitor effectiveness." But how can you measure performance when you do not know what to measure against? By being on-site and performing the systems integration processes, real baseline values are established to effect real KPI measured performance – data that U.S. Flan does not have. The consultant states that orders are placed electronically, but with the 3PMRO supplier on-site, U.S. Flan stops placing orders altogether. So, there's no need for e-procurement.

Based on the two proposals, U.S. Flan chose the on-site provider because the consultant recommends the change, gets paid for the knowledge and moves on. Consultants do not actually do what they recommend; performance is the responsibility of the consultant's client. In comparison, the on-site supplier does not get paid until the process change is implemented and operating (i.e., the supplier must perform before the client extends payment for services proposed).

# AGGREGATING MRO FOR RELIABILITY AND PROFIT

MRO supplies represent an opportunity to recoup hidden costs, as well as identify time-consuming profit drags on a reliable plant. However, such opportunities for necessary improvements generally go unnoticed.

Here is a case study of a pharmaceutical manufacturer with high production standards. To produce a reliable and profitable product, the company demands adherence to those standards from its production and maintenance people.

## THE PROBLEM

In a study of all operating functions to identify waste, inefficiencies, duplicated costs and opportunities for improvement, the company realized the cost of not having parts on hand when needed was a major deterrent to plant efficiencies.

Due to an incomplete process, various departments created separate "sub-storerooms" to store spare parts and avoid the dreaded downtime. This situation caused inventory duplications, augmented by a lack of communications of data among departments. Parts stored in one area but needed in another were reordered unnecessarily, causing delays and costs. So, the problem became defined: Reliability and plant profits were being negatively affected by the current MRO operation.

## THE SOLUTION

It was determined that by centralizing all parts into a controlled storeroom and creating enriched content, locations and parts availability could be communicated to all departments. With rightsized inventory, fill rate goals were set at ninety-six percent, critical spares at one hundred percent and all substocks, including duplications, were eliminated or unnecessary due to the newfound reliability of the storeroom. The company was on track to recover eight percent of inventory investment in the first year.

With consolidated purchases, the total price of parts was substantially reduced. Invoice processing costs plummeted, with just twenty-four transactions per year required from a previous paper burden of ninety-five thousand transactions. In addition, the new process reduced incoming freight costs by two and five tenths percent.

*The most significant benefit accrued is the coordination of stores' activity with maintenance reliability programs.* By making stores' activities a part of maintenance, reliability soars with waste controlled and intelligence sharing. These activities include administration of data relating to FMEA, MTTR and RCA.

## THE CONSIDERATION

It was decided to partner with a company whose core competence was the end-to-end process of MRO. There are two types of companies offering services to improve MRO operations for industrial consumers of MRO.

1. Companies that charge a fee to teach how to set up and redesign stores' operations. These companies do not physically operate the stores' function after implementing their services. They teach and leave.
2. Companies that perform all the services necessary to implement the desired change and then continue to perform the function of total MRO stores management on-site. These companies are responsible for achieving the stated goals of change and sustaining the change over the contract period.

# CONCLUSION

In this case study, the selected path was contracting with an MRO expert whose core competency is on-site stores management, including a history of success in regulated industry. During the solution assessment, the company and the MRO provider developed a scope of work that would deliver the company's total cost of ownership reduction and performance goals. This established the contract's financial and non-financial goals supported by measured KPI performance.

With mutual agreement, the program was implemented (i.e., initiating the statement of work, opening day occurred on time and the benefits began).

The problem was resolved, reliability was restored, total cost of ownership was at optimum and sustained, precious time was recovered and management was relieved of previous MRO burdens.

# SUMMARY

*"MRO remains the last bastion of uncontrolled expense in the world of commerce"*
– Plato

The complexities of MRO situations are universal among industries, no matter how diverse the product. A processor of fish will have the same MRO considerations and hidden cost problems as the MRO store in the *Washington Post*, and much of the same parts in inventory. Experience shows that MRO change represents the highest percentage cost recovery opportunity available to American industry today.

The opportunity largely goes unrealized for myriad of reasons, among them disagreement among disciplines, entrenched suppliers, antiquated selection processes, perceived opportunity costs (unknown ROI) and the biggie, lack of know-how.

The maintenance director of a large chemical company was assigned the responsibility of establishing reliability in its MRO stores' operation. The director confided that he could strip down every asset in the plant and put it back together better than it was. In the same breath, he lamented that he had no idea how to manage MRO; he was an engineer with two degrees, not a hardware store manager.

This is the essence of MRO today (yesterday, too) in that the people in charge do not have all the skill sets or the time/inclination to capture all the opportunities that are available to be captured.

If you find yourself saying:

"MRO is not our core competency; we excel in all things except for managing our MRO."

"There is nothing we can do about MRO, so we must put up with the vagaries of uncontrolled and unreliable MRO supply."

***Why are you still in the MRO business?***

# EPILOGUE

In this book, the use of the fictional company U.S. Flan simulates real scenarios that occur to real companies in the complex world of MRO. One of the leaders at U.S. Flan was T.M. Doyle, Director of Procurement.

Although the names are fictitious, the situations described are real and did occur within a real company; there was a real T.M. Doyle.

U.S. Flan, with T.M. Doyle in the lead as director of procurement, was the first company to implement a full-scale, on-site third-party MRO program utilizing a fledgling supply company whose sole source of income was derived from operating, stocking, issuing and controlling MRO storerooms on-site. The measured effects of the jointly created scope of work provided significant benefits for U.S. Flan for decades.

T.M. Doyle had both the vision and the fortitude to initiate and sustain MRO change from a long-standing, ingrained procedure that had been followed since the Industrial Revolution.

T.M., along with his provider, changed the industrial distribution industry.

# ABOUT THE AUTHOR

## George E. Krauter

eorge Krauter was the Founder, President and CEO of Industrial Systems Associates before his retirement. He currently serves as Vice President for Storeroom Solutions, Inc., Radnor, PA. Mr. Krauter is recognized as the originator of the industrial supply chain concept that became known as integrated supply.

He has participated as a guest speaker at Reliability 2.0, ISM Annual Indirect Procurement Conference, International Maintenance Conference (IMC), The Conference Board's President's Council and events for APICS, SMRP and ISM professional chapters.

Mr. Krauter is recognized as an authority on methods to optimize costs and achieve reliable, maintenance-connected MRO storerooms. He has published his experiences in *Uptime Magazine, Food Manufacturing, My Purchasing Center, Industrial Maintenance & Plant Operation (IMPO)* and *Supply & Demand Chain Executive.*

Mr. Krauter holds a B.A. and M.B.A.A. from Temple University and has conducted seminars internationally in Oslo, Abu Dhabi, Puerto Rico and Mexico, as well as sessions at Duke University, MIT, Howard University and Temple University.

He lives in Bucks County, PA, with his wife Joyce; all grandkids live within eating distance.

# uptime®Elements™
## A Reliability Framework for Asset Performance

*This book falls under Work Execution Management*

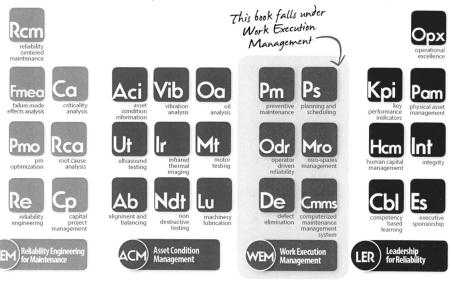

**Rcm** reliability centered maintenance

**Opx** operational excellence

**Fmea** failure mode effects analysis — **Ca** criticality analysis

**Aci** asset condition information — **Vib** vibration analysis — **Oa** oil analysis

**Pm** preventive maintenance — **Ps** planning and scheduling

**Kpi** key performance indicators — **Pam** physical asset management

**Pmo** pm optimization — **Rca** root cause analysis

**Ut** ultrasound testing — **Ir** infrared thermal imaging — **Mt** motor testing

**Odr** operator driven reliability — **Mro** mro-spares management

**Hcm** human capital management — **Int** integrity

**Re** reliability engineering — **Cp** capital project management

**Ab** alignment and balancing — **Ndt** non destructive testing — **Lu** machinery lubrication

**De** defect elimination — **Cmms** computerized maintenance management system

**Cbl** competency based learning — **Es** executive sponsorship

**REM** Reliability Engineering for Maintenance

**ACM** Asset Condition Management

**WEM** Work Execution Management

**LER** Leadership for Reliability

### Reliabilityweb.com's Asset Management Timeline

**AM** Asset Management — Business Needs Analysis — Asset Plan — Design — Create — Operate / Maintain — Modify/Upgrade / Dispose

Asset Lifecycle

Reliabilityweb.com® and Uptime® Magazine Mission: To make the people we serve safer and more successful.
One way we support this mission is to suggest a reliability system for asset performance management as pictured above.
Our use of the Uptime Elements is designed to assist you in categorizing and organizing your own Body of Knowledge (BoK),
whether it be through training, articles, books, or webinars. Our hope is to make YOU safer and more successful.

# About Reliabilityweb.com

Created in 1999, Reliabilityweb.com provides educational information and peer-to-peer networking opportunities that enable safe and effective maintenance reliability and asset management for organizations around the world.

## Activities Include:

**Reliabilityweb.com** (www.reliabilityweb.com) includes educational articles, tips, video presentations, an industry event calendar and industry news. Updates are available through free email subscriptions and RSS feeds. **Confiabilidad.net** is a mirror site that is available in Spanish at www.confiabilidad.net

**Uptime Magazine** (www.uptimemagazine.com) is a bi-monthly magazine launched in 2005 that is highly prized by the maintenance reliability and asset management community. Editions are obtainable in print, online, digital, Kindle and through the iPad/iPhone app.

## Reliability Leadership Institute Conferences and Training Events

(www.maintenanceconference.com) offer events that range from unique, focused-training workshops and seminars to small focused conferences to large industry-wide events, including the International Maintenance Conference and The RELIABILITY Conference.

**MRO-Zone Bookstore** (www.mro-zone.com) is an online bookstore offering a maintenance reliability and asset management focused library of books, DVDs and CDs published by Reliabilityweb.com.

## Association of Asset Management Professionals

(www.maintenance.org) is a member organization and online community that encourages professional development and certification and supports information exchange and learning with 10,000+ members worldwide.

### A Word About Social Good

Reliabilityweb.com is mission driven to deliver value and social good to the maintenance reliability and asset management communities. *Doing good work and making profit is not inconsistent*, and as a result of Reliabilityweb.com's mission-driven focus, financial stability and success has been the outcome. For over a decade, Reliabilityweb.com's positive contributions and commitment to the maintenance reliability and asset management communities have been unmatched.

### Other Causes

Reliabilityweb.com has financially contributed to include industry associations, such as SMRP, AFE, STLE, ASME and ASTM, and community charities, including the Salvation Army, American Red Cross, Wounded Warrior Project, Paralyzed Veterans of America and the Autism Society of America. In addition, we are proud supporters of our U.S. Troops and first responders who protect our freedoms and way of life. That is only possible by being a for-profit company that pays taxes.

I hope you will get involved with and explore the many resources that are available to you through the Reliabilityweb.com network.

Warmest regards,
Terrence O'Hanlon
CEO, Reliabilityweb.com